WE ALCOTTS

WE ALCOTTS

·

The story of
Louisa M. Alcott's family
as seen through the eyes of
"Marmee," mother of
Little Women

·

AILEEN FISHER & OLIVE RABE

decorations by Ellen Raskin

ATHENEUM   1969   NEW YORK

Grateful acknowledgment is made to Little, Brown and Company for permission to use a number of quotations from *Louisa May Alcott, Her Life, Letters and Journals,* by Ednah D. Cheney; *The Journals of Bronson Alcott,* edited by Odell Shepard; *Pedlar's Progress,* by Odell Shepard; and *Concord Days,* by A. Bronson Alcott.

Library of Congress Catalog Card Number 68-18445
Published simultaneously in Canada
by McClelland & Stewart Ltd.
Manufactured in the United States of America
Printed by Halliday Lithograph Corporation,
West Hanover, Massachusetts
Bound by The Book Press, Inc., Brattleboro, Vermont
Designed by Judith Lerner
First Printing July 1968
Second Printing February 1969
Third Printing September 1969

AUTHOR'S NOTE

SINCE MOST OF THE RESPONSIBILITY for keeping the
Alcott household together rested on the shoulders of
Abba May Alcott, the "Marmee" of *Little Women*,
it seemed to us appropriate to tell the story of the
family from her point of view. The story is based on
the journals, letters, and other writings of the Alcotts
as well as on those of friends and relatives; also on
critical studies of the Alcott family that have been
published down the years. We are especially grateful
to Professor Odell Shepard for condensing the fifty
volumes of Bronson Alcott's handwritten journals into
shortened readable form.

All the people in the story are real people, all places
are real places, and all situations rooted in actual happenings. Much of the dialogue incorporates sentences,

words, and phrases from writings of the Alcotts, Ralph Waldo Emerson, Henry Thoreau, and others. Dialogue not actually quoted we have tried to key to the spirit of the times and the feelings of the speakers as shown by the record of their actions and reactions.

A.F. AND O.R.

"Human life is a very simple matter. Breath, bread, health, a hearthstone, a fountain, fruits, a few garden seeds and room to plant them in, a wife and children, a friend or two of either sex, conversation, neighbours, and a task life-long given from within—these are contentment and a great estate. On these gifts follow all others . . ."

A. BRONSON ALCOTT
JOURNAL, MAY 20, 1856

WE ALCOTTS

CHAPTER 1

I SHALL NEVER FORGET the 8th of August, 1827, the day I first met Mr. Alcott. I was visiting my brother, the Reverend Samuel May, at his parsonage in Connecticut, as an escape from the strangeness of my old home in Boston after my father's second marriage. Things had not been going too well for me. I no longer felt needed by my father. My two sisters had married and established homes of their own, and my brother Sam, upon whom I depended for intellectual companionship, no longer lived in Boston. I had no occupation. Though I could play the piano and sing, in the tradition of the May family, I was not accomplished enough to think of making music a career.

I was nearing my twenty-seventh birthday, an age when most women had husbands and children and homes of their own. But I had not been fortunate enough to find any man who interested me enough for me to cast my lot with his for life. The road into my future looked cold and uninviting.

"We may be favored with some stimulating conversation the next few days," my brother Sam said one morning, as he and his wife Lu and I sat at the breakfast table. "I have invited Mr. Bronson Alcott for a visit." He turned to me. "I've written you something about his advanced ideas of teaching children, haven't I, Abba?"

"Indeed you have. But I haven't the background to appreciate them fully."

"Sam thinks we could make good use of some Alcott theories in our school here," Lu put in. "He is, in fact, quite *intense* about it."

"Where is Mr. Alcott's school?" I asked.

"He's had at least two," answered Sam. "The latest at Cheshire, just fifty miles from here, was a most unusual school. That's what makes me eager to hear more of his theories. Unfortunately he had to close the school in June, after only two years, although it had the reputation of being the best school for children in the state of Connecticut."

"And still it wasn't a success?"

"So far as the children went, yes. He achieved amazing results. But the parents . . ." My brother shook his head. "They objected to every new idea, the old was good enough for them. And they couldn't understand children actually liking a teacher and wanting to go to school. Something must be wrong, they felt. They thought the rod ought to be more in evidence. I'm afraid Mr. Alcott is a generation or two ahead of his time."

"That ought to make him interesting to talk to," I said, "if he isn't too old and grim and bespectacled."

My brother had prepared me for Mr. Alcott's advanced ideas, but he had not prepared me for the striking figure and charming manners of the young educator, just a year older than I. My first and lasting impression was of a tall, slender, handsome man with an attractive pucker in his chin. His blue eyes fairly glowed whenever he talked earnestly about things close to his heart. And his voice! Never had I listened to such a melodious, appealing voice. That voice, coupled with his appearance and his amazing flow of ideas, set him apart from all men I had ever met. I was under his spell at once.

I could see that Sam was attracted to Mr. Alcott, too—so much so that he told me afterward that only once before had he been so immediately taken possession of by any man. "He seemed to me a born sage and saint," he said.

Bit by bit, during the week of his visit, we learned about Bronson Alcott and his theories of education, and we were amazed and charmed. How a boy born on a worn-out Connecticut farm, educated meagerly in the district schools, could turn into such a cultured

5

young man baffled us. My brother, a graduate of Harvard, put the question hesitantly. "How . . . how . . . ?"

Mr. Alcott smiled. "A pedlar has a chance to learn a great deal."

"A pedlar!" I exclaimed.

"For four years I peddled needles and thread and ribbons and tin goods in Virginia and the Carolinas. It gave me a chance to dip into the library of many a southern planter. It opened doors to courtliness and conversation, and gave me a chance to satisfy my hunger for books."

Mr. Alcott told us how even as a boy he had rebelled at being confined for hours on end in a stuffy schoolroom, where he had to sit on a backless bench. He rebelled, too, against the noise of "blab" reading and reciting. And he lived in fear of the schoolmaster's rod. "I knew, even then, there must be a better way," he said.

Pressed by Sam, he went on to tell about the school at Cheshire that had attracted so much attention. "I introduced a number of changes. I saw to it that the school was fitted out with blackboards and slates, and separate desks instead of benches. And books! I built up a library there of a hundred and sixty-five books for the pupils to borrow and their parents, too. My aim was to develop all sides of a child's nature, with special emphasis on imagination."

My brother was listening eagerly. "Just what we

need here," he exclaimed. "But how did you manage to get the parents to pay for all those improvements?"

"I didn't," Mr. Alcott confessed. "I paid for them myself, out of my salary. And some of the parents objected, even so."

I looked at him with a heart full of respect and admiration. Here was a man with ideals. Here was a man willing to spend his own money, his own small earnings, to carry out his ideals. Here was a man . . .

Mr. Alcott had a reserved, bashful way with women, except when talk carried us above personalities into the Country of the Mind, as he called it. But in spite of his reserve, I sensed how he felt about me before the visit was over. There was no question how I felt about him. He told me when we parted that he had never before talked so fully to a woman with my background, and that he appreciated my straightforwardness and frankness in stating my opinions. And he said he quite agreed with me that woman's position was lower than it should be.

"It does you honor to say so," I replied quickly.

Though we did not see each other again for months, I had letters to look forward to, and reading to do. For years I had concentrated on history. But now I turned my full attention to methods of education, reading book after book that Mr. Alcott suggested. I was fascinated, especially by the ideas of Pestalozzi, an outstanding Swiss educator whom Mr. Alcott greatly admired.

In the fall I mentioned in a letter that I thought Boston was the place for a man of Mr. Alcott's ability, and my brother was even more urgent about a move to Boston. But Mr. Alcott had already agreed to teach a five-month term at Bristol, Connecticut. I hoped fervently that he would gain as much recognition in educational circles for his work at Bristol as he had at Cheshire. My brother had just received a copy of William Russell's *American Journal of Education* in which there was an article on the Cheshire school by A. Bronson Alcott. I devoured it.

As it turned out Mr. Alcott had a difficult time at Bristol because of opposition from hostile religious groups. After several months he wrote that he had, at least, learned one thing—that he had to use great care to introduce improvements gradually. Hampered at every turn, he carried on through the term with frustration and disappointment.

Months passed before we met again. But eventually Mr. Alcott did come to Boston to start a new type of children's school with the help of my brother and some friends. I went about with a song in my heart. With Mr. Alcott living in Boston, we could see each other often.

The first time he spent an evening in my old home on Federal Court, I noticed that he seemed somewhat overawed by our large and comfortable house surrounded by orchard and garden. And he seemed even more overawed by the courtly appearance of my tall and impressive father, Col. Joseph May. But fortunately the two men fell into easy conversation and the effect of Father's striking appearance soon wore off. They talked on and on about the books they both loved and the good causes they believed in. Father talked well, almost as well as our visitor I thought; they drew each other out and got along famously.

Unfortunately Mr. Alcott did not have the opportunity of knowing my mother except through my eyes, for she had died a few years before. Her family, the Sewalls, were prominent among the old families of Boston, as was the May family on my father's side, and my cousin Samuel Sewall, a Boston lawyer, soon became a staunch friend and admirer of Bronson Alcott.

To my great delight Mr. Alcott was captivated by Boston, not so much by its picturesque cobblestone streets and dignified colonial houses, as by its intellectual atmosphere, which was more bracing to him than the smell of the sea. He called Boston the capitol of the Country of the Mind, the City that was set on High, and I heartily agreed.

I found myself becoming more and more involved with the life and thoughts of Bronson Alcott as the weeks and months went by. But still he did not speak out what I had every reason to believe was in his mind.

CHAPTER 2

AFTER MONTHS OF COMPANIONSHIP, Mr. Alcott asked me to read some entries in his Journal. I held my breath as I read, for they were about Miss Abba May! Now at last I found out what I had long suspected. He loved me, yet hesitated to ask me to marry him. His poverty stood in the way, and the feeling that he was an unknown socially. Learning this, I almost regretted being a member of a family of respected social standing.

Mr. Alcott had me read those entries in his Journal to break down the economic barrier between us. And, of course, it did. Why should we be distressed about poverty, either of us? Why should we let it concern us when we had so many other worthwhile things to fill our minds?

After finding out how I felt about sharing his life, poverty and all, he finally found it easy enough to ask me to marry him. We took long walks together through the beautiful countryside around Boston, but I must confess that we saw all too little of the scenery, so engrossed were we in our dreams for making the world over.

I wrote to my brother that I thought Mr. Alcott qualified in every way to make me happy. We supplemented each other. He was moderate, I impetuous. He was modest and humble, I forward and arbitrary. He was poor, but we were both industrious. From the first we had a meeting of the minds on matters of importance—education, slavery, women's rights, books. I pointed all this out and told my brother that I had never felt so happy in my life. To have someone to love and something to live for—what more could life offer?

I knew my brother felt as I did, for he had written me: "Don't distress yourself about his poverty. His mind and heart are so much occupied with other things that poverty and riches do not seem to concern him."

Mr. Alcott had established a school in Boston for boys between three and seven years old, all from well-to-do families. As the months went by, the school attracted more and more favorable attention. Visitors came in such numbers that Mr. Alcott sometimes feared they would interfere with his work. But even though the school was such a success, his earnings were not large, and for lack of money our marriage kept being delayed.

Late one afternoon on a gray chilly day at the end of 1829, Mr. Alcott called for me to walk with him. "I have something to tell you," he confided cheerfully as we started off toward the hills. "Today I was asked to start another school."

"And give up the Tremont Street School?"

"Yes. And be paid more than twice what I am getting now."

More than twice! "Oh, Mr. Alcott!" I exclaimed eagerly.

"That is what I wanted to talk about, Miss May. I refused the offer immediately."

My heart sank, but I knew there must be some good reason. I remained silent.

"The Boston followers of Robert Owen asked me to start a school for their children," Mr. Alcott went on. "At first the idea excited me. As you know, I am a great admirer of Robert Owen."

Yes, I knew. Mr. Alcott had often expressed interest in the Scotch socialist who had established an experimental community at New Harmony, Indiana, several years before. Unfortunately the project had to be abandoned, but Mr. Alcott still saw virtue in the plan for a cooperative community and thought it could be worked out. "You were not to have a free hand?" I asked.

"I was to teach the children only what could be

demonstrated to their senses and perceptions. I was not to appeal to the soul of a child, to his imagination. I was not to attempt to mold character—the very things that mean most to me."

"You did right to refuse the offer, Mr. Alcott," I said with finality. What did money matter if he had to compromise with his principles? I could but admire him the more for not being tempted, for being willing to make any sacrifice to uphold his ideals. I felt uplifted and proud to be engaged to a man like Bronson Alcott.

Finally, money or no money, the day of our marriage arrived.

May is a beautiful month for a New England wedding. On the 23rd of May, 1830, when Bronson Alcott and I stood before the Rev. Greenwood in King's Chapel, spring was in the air, and the sound of birdsong came in through an open window. Spring is always a time of hope, and doubly so when one embarks on a new adventure with a loved companion.

Someone described us as a singularly handsome pair on that wedding day, and the description fit Mr. Alcott to the full. He wore white trousers with straps to hold them under his boots, a blue broadcloth swallowtail, a bell-shaped hat of white beaver, and he carried an ivory-headed cane. I had on a plaid silk dress with a small hoop in the skirt and big puffed sleeves. My skirt was about six inches from the floor, revealing my white stockings and black sandals; and my broad-brimmed black beaver hat was decked out with a big bow of plaid ribbon to match my dress.

We spent our first months in rented rooms in Boston, and I well remember writing Lu, Brother Sam's wife, that I hoped we could go through life infected by the lunacy that possessed us then. Happily, we were able to spend a great deal of time together, for Mr. Alcott continued teaching in the school he had started, and I worked with him there part of the time.

What busy days those were! Having lived in Boston all my life, I of course knew many people, and I was eager to have my husband meet those who shared our interests and aspirations. Foremost among them was my dear friend Lydia Maria Child. Maria, as I always called her, was one of the most accomplished women I knew. Younger than I by more than a year, she had already achieved national recognition for her writing. Even before I met Bronson Alcott, she had had two popular novels to her credit and had started a children's magazine that appeared twice a month. She and her husband David Child were ardent crusaders for the antislavery cause, and soon we were swept into active participation in the movement, too, through my brother and my cousin Samuel Sewall.

I had numerous relatives in Boston among the Mays, Sewalls, Quincys, and Windships to whom I wanted to show off my new husband. Then there were visitors at the school to entertain. And my husband, though a newcomer to the city, had made friends of his own. Among them two stood out—William Russell, an Englishman of culture and education who had established a school near Boston, and Miss Elizabeth Peabody, his assistant.

Miss Peabody intrigued us both. A few years younger than I, she had spent her childhood in Salem. Now, in 1830, she was well-known in the intellectual circles of Boston as a teacher of note and as secretary to Dr. William Ellery Channing, foremost Unitarian minister in the city.

"She has a mind of superior order," my husband remarked after we had taken tea with her one afternoon. The admiration was mutual, for Miss Peabody confided to me that my husband had more genius for education than anyone she ever saw.

Two months after our marriage we received an unexpected wedding present that quite overshadowed all the beautiful gifts that had come our way. I had thought that the lovely old pieces of furniture from the Mays, and the beautiful sterling silver dish from my cousin Hannah Robie, and some exquisite chinaware, could not be surpassed. But an anonymous gift of two thousand dollars made us gasp with unbelief and pleasure. Was it Father's way of telling us that he approved heartily of the marriage? I wondered. Or had some old friend of the family come to our rescue?

We never found out who sent the money, but it was a godsend to us. I was glad that my husband wanted to use a third of it to pay back with interest a long-standing debt to his father. But I doubted the wisdom of spending two hundred and fifty dollars of what was left for printing a thousand copies of an essay Mr. Alcott had written on the principles of teaching children. Later I was glad that I held my peace. My husband's pleasure at seeing his essay in print made me feel a little guilty that I had not been wholeheartedly in favor.

Early that fall Brother Sam came to Boston, bringing along a letter he had received from William Lloyd Garrison, a young crusader against slavery. Mr. Garrison planned to make three speeches in Boston that week, and Sam was eager to hear him. So was our cousin Samuel Sewall. They took my husband along with them to the first Garrison meeting.

Mr. Alcott was so impressed by Mr. Garrison that he asked him and the two Samuels to come home with him after the lecture for further talk. I joined them, and we talked until after midnight. Mr. Garrison told us of his plan to start an antislavery paper in Boston.

"I propose to call it the *Liberator*," he said.

Cousin Samuel shook his head. "The name is too provoking."

"Provoking!" cried Mr. Garrison. "That's just what I want it to be. Slavery has already lasted for more than two hundred years in these United States. It is *time* we did something provoking. As for me, I am prepared to make any sacrifice to open people's eyes and show them the tyranny of our laws."

We were all swept away by Mr. Garrison's enthusiasm for immediate action on the slavery issue. Soon afterward my brother, my cousin, my husband and others met with Mr. Garrison and formed an antislavery society.

Meanwhile my husband had been distributing copies of his pamphlet about educating children. Many favorable comments reached us. But best of all, one day he came hurrying into the boardinghouse where we were living and grasped my hands, saying, "A great piece of good fortune, my dear! We are going to move . . . to a home of our own."

"But we are well situated here, within walking distance of your school. And can we afford to take a house?"

"Indeed we can. If you favor the plan, we shall be on our way to Germantown, Pennsylvania, as soon as possible."

I looked at him in consternation, I who thought Boston the hub of the universe. "Germantown?"

"Wait till you hear. Mr. Haines, a wealthy Quaker from Germantown, came to visit the school today. He had read my essay and wanted to see my teaching principles put into practice. At once he knew that we were in complete agreement. Brother Haines has seven children . . ."

"And he wants you to tutor them? To give up your school? And your fine assistant Mr. Russell?"

My husband smiled indulgently. "He wants Mr.

Russell and me to start a school in Germantown which his children and others of the community can attend. Mr. Haines will finance the school, and I will be on a salary . . . a good salary. And we are to have a home of our own. I see it as a step ahead, my dear. A definite step ahead."

CHAPTER 3

GERMANTOWN TURNED OUT to be a much pleasanter place than I expected. Its well-built colonial houses clustering along the old Great Road on the outskirts of Philadelphia gave it charm and distinction. A goodly number of its citizens were Quakers, and their simplicity of manner appealed to both Mr. Alcott and me. They were invariably dignified and tranquil, the wealthy ones not in the least spoiled by their wealth. Boston seemed far away; yet from the first I felt little deprivation in being away from it.

Spring of 1831 found us well settled in a pleasant square house that Mr. Haines bought, with living quarters for us and rooms for the school and boarding pupils. Pine Place we called it, instead of its old name The Rookery. Though situated on the main street of the village, the house had an air of the country about it, with its large grounds and garden of more than an acre. The garden was lined with berry bushes, the winding walk shaded by pines, cedars, firs, and fruit trees. I wrote enthusiastically to my father, calling Pine Place our little paradise, and telling him that my imagination had never pictured so perfect a residence.

My husband and Mr. Russell were still busy completing plans for the school and preparing for the first classes when something happened that would in time give my husband a chance to learn more about children than he could possibly learn in a schoolroom. Our first child was born! At eleven o'clock on the evening of March 16, Anna Bronson Alcott gave her first cry.

A few minutes later my husband leaned over my bed. "A lovely blonde, blue-eyed girl," he said. I could tell that he was tingling with suppressed excitement, even though he spoke softly. "What a new and interesting event in our lives, Abba! I am filled with the greatest joy and gratitude."

I reached for his hand. "An Alcott like you—blonde and blue-eyed. Not a dark-haired, dark-skinned May like her mother." I smiled at him and closed my eyes happily. He had not given a hint of disappointment that his first child was not a son.

From the evening of Anna's birth, my husband made detailed observations of her, writing them down in his record book. As time went on, I doubted if any child had ever been watched more closely and analyzed more fully than our little daughter. He called his record "An Historical Account of the Development of the Intellect and Moral Conduct of My Little Girl," which I thought rather a long title for one so small. At first I smiled away the detailed observations as a passing whim, but as the pages piled up week after week, I became almost as much interested in the record as my husband.

By the time our first wedding anniversary came in May, I was feeling strong again, Anna was prospering, our home hummed with happiness, and the school was off to a good start. With great gratitude to my father for his quick acceptance of Mr. Alcott as a man of superior worth and intellect, I wrote to him on our anniversary day, telling him that he had never seen a daughter or a son more happily married than I.

Soon my husband and I became members of a group that met on Saturday evenings for conversation and a social hour. My husband, with his natural gift for conversation and his unusually pleasing voice, became a leader of the group before many weeks passed.

Throughout all the weeks and months of preparation for the school, Mr. Alcott found our benefactor Mr. Haines a pleasure to work with. Not only were they in complete agreement on the basic principles of teaching, but on the philosophy of simple living. More than once I thought that my husband might well have been born a Quaker . . . his beliefs fitted so well into theirs. As for me, the entire Haines family was a joy and a delight. They lived about a mile from us on a fine old farm in a big house, plain but dignified. Mrs. Haines, the experienced mother of seven lively children, was generous in giving me advice about the care and rearing of our little daughter, a task for which I felt poorly prepared.

In some ways Anna's father was a better "mother" than I. He had infinite patience and gentleness, and a natural skill in handling children. My eagerness to read sometimes made me resentful of seemingly endless household tasks. But my husband could spend hours with the baby in perfect contentment, making his endless researches. By the time Anna was five months old he had filled a whole volume with his observations.

Soon twenty children were attending the school, a few of them boarding pupils. With the school right in the house, I was able to help with the music and other activities. My husband kept busy from morning till night with his teaching, his attention to Anna, and his voluminous reading, in which he was spurred on by Mr. Russell.

It was a full and happy summer. And I was able to put a little money aside for emergencies.

Living with us at the school as he did, Mr. Russell became almost a member of our family. We felt it a privilege to get to know him intimately. He was still editor of the *American Journal of Education,* which my husband had read carefully even before he knew him. And, of course, he had taught in Mr. Alcott's school in Boston. But in Germantown there was less social activity and the two men had a chance to talk by the hour about books and ideas. As I listened to them, I realized more fully than ever that to one who loves to talk, conversation is the life blood of a day's living.

Mr. Russell was a great help to my husband in organizing his ideas. Bronson Alcott's ideas often came to him in a flash of inspiration, but he lacked the training in logic to present them most effectively. Mr. Russell, an unusually logical thinker, spent many hours training my husband in logic.

By fall the school had as many children as the two men could handle. And then, suddenly, without any warning, our cup of happiness cracked.

On a fluttering October day when the trees in Germantown and the surrounding countryside were putting on a glorious display of color, when nothing but brightness and joy should have been abroad, news came from the farmhouse down the road that Mr. Haines had died. We were stunned. My heart went out at once to my dear friend Mrs. Haines, left with the responsibility of rearing seven children and running the big farm.

Mr. Alcott broke into my thoughts. "He had such an interest in the school. We were just beginning to get results . . ."

The school! What would happen to the school now? "Surely Mr. Haines made some provision for the school to continue," I said, grasping at hope.

But our good friend had died so suddenly, he had made no provision whatever for the school. Fees from enrollment fell far short of meeting expenses. I tried to keep my apprehension to myself, yet I did not see how the school could continue without Mr. Haines' generous support.

As usual Mr. Alcott was optimistic, unperturbed. "The school will go on," he said. "Perhaps someone else will offer to help. In the meantime we must cut expenses."

We tried to hold the school together, even though enrollment fell off. We cut expenses. Mr. Russell left for Philadelphia to start a girls' school and to work on his *Journal*, leaving Mr. Alcott with a long list of books to read. Pine Place was still ours to use, and we had a little income from boarding pupils, but now our future was a question mark instead of the exclamation mark of joy it had been that first handful of months.

Somehow, with the help of our Quaker friends, we managed to get through that winter and the following summer without going into debt. Fall came, and the school was in even worse straits.

Then on November 29, Mr. Alcott's thirty-third birthday, our second child was born. Another girl. We named her Louisa May after my favorite sister, who had died the year before. And little Louisa, dark of hair and skin, was indeed a May, as Anna was an Alcott.

In high spirits Bronson wrote to my father, announcing the birth of our new daughter. He read me the letter before mailing it, and I was gratified to hear that he made the announcement "with great pleasure," although he must have wanted a son.

As with Anna, he started at once making observations of Louisa. But this time his records were not quite so voluminous. Occasionally he read me excerpts from his notes, asking my reactions. I remember that he called Louisa a "guileless creature, the child of instinct," even when she was a very small baby. More than once he thought her obstinate, but admitted that this very obstinacy gave her a strength that might some day be a powerful asset in her life.

Not long after the birth of Louisa, I could sense that the father of two lively daughters was restlessly searching for some stimulating mental activity. The school had dwindled to practically nothing. Mr. Russell was busy in Philadelphia, and my husband missed the intellectual exchange with him. In addition, our family needed some income.

With the coming of spring, Mr. Alcott decided to go to Philadelphia to open a school. "You must stay here in Germantown with the children where the air is fresh and healthful," he told me. "I will come often on weekends. My hope is to get an inexpensive room near the library so I can read and study when I am not teaching. Oh, I have so much to read, Abba. I wonder if I can ever make up for my lack of formal education." I encouraged him to go, though I dreaded to think of Pine Place without him.

He found a fourth-floor attic room on Library Street, with one little window that looked out on the City Library and the Athenaeum. His description of it made me wince; it was starkly furnished with a bed, a washstand, two chairs, and a trunk for his clothes. "But my books make it look homelike," he assured me. "And it matters little, after all, so long as there is food for the mind and comfort for the heart. I am comforted to know that you and the children are well and happy in Germantown."

My days were full and busy, but the weeks seemed long, the weekends all too short. In the summer, when school was out, Mr. Alcott stayed on in his hot little room, reading insatiably. I quite understood his craving for books and his need for time and quiet, and agreed that he was pursuing the best course, lonely though I often felt without him.

Meanwhile things were happening on a broader front, beyond the immediate activities of the Alcott family. My friend Maria Child was writing me anxious and fiery letters about a situation that had come up in Connecticut. A young Quaker woman, Prudence Crandall, had a school for girls at Canterbury. When she admitted a Negro girl, the townspeople raised a storm of protest. Not to be intimidated, Miss Crandall decided to start a school for Negroes only.

Maria wrote that the opposition was immediate and violent. "They are trying to intimidate Prudence Crandall in every possible way. They filled her well with refuse. They forbade her to enter the church. They attacked her house and threatened to burn it. Worst of all, Abba, they have pushed an act through the Connecticut legislature making it illegal for anyone to establish a school for colored people without the consent of the townspeople. Now the latest is that Prudence Crandall has been arrested, under this new law, and her case is attracting wide attention in Abolitionist circles."

I could not help wondering what action my brother Sam was taking.

My question was soon answered in a hurried note from Maria. "Your brother and Arthur Tappan have taken up the cause of Prudence Crandall. Now I am sure the fight will not be lost. Why should Negroes not be allowed to get an education? I have decided to write a little book about it myself, even though the cause is unpopular with the reading public and my reputation as a writer will suffer."

Late that fall of 1833 Maria sent me a copy of her *Appeal* which had been hurried through the press. I glowed with pleasure when I saw that she had dedicated the book to the Reverend Samuel J. May, for his defense of Prudence Crandall.

I found Maria's *Appeal* a stirring piece of work. But I couldn't help wondering what would happen to her reputation as a popular writer.

All too soon she was made to suffer for her stand against race prejudice. She lost her membership in the Boston Athenaeum. Doors to the houses of former friends were shut in her face. Sales of her other books, mostly popular novels, plummeted. The children's magazine, *Juvenile Miscellany*, which she had started seven years before, died a quick death. Yet I was sure that the many converts her *Appeal* made compensated her for everything.

Meanwhile our own sheltered life moved along smoothly. My husband profited immensely from his summer of study in Philadelphia. He became greatly excited over his discovery of Plato. And Coleridge's *Aids to Reflection* marked an epoch in his mental career. He read it once every year after that, and rated it next to *Pilgrim's Progress* among the treasured books of his choice. But through all his discoveries in the world of ideas, no book ever swept him off his feet or changed the direction of his thinking. For the most part the new authors were most valuable in confirming his own ideas and in increasing his deep respect for the noble minds of all ages.

We had little money during our last two years in Germantown. But we had much happiness in our little family and in knowing that we were not stagnating mentally. Through all the uncertainty over the school, my husband managed to keep cheerful. "Something will work out," he kept saying. "Fortunately our wants are few."

He might have spent an entire second summer in his stifling room had not Mr. Russell and other friends urged him to go back to Boston to start another school. They prepared the way for him. At the suggestion of Dr. Channing, Miss Elizabeth Peabody even rounded up a number of prospective pupils. And so in midsummer, 1834, Bronson Alcott gave up his attic room, sent me and the girls to visit Brother Sam in Connecticut, and went to Boston to see about the school.

I was relieved. I felt that Mr. Alcott never would do well as a teacher in Philadelphia. Boston was different. Surely that was where our fortune lay, even though we would have to borrow money to move back after a little more than three years away.

CHAPTER 4

EARLY IN SEPTEMBER Mr. Alcott came to gather up his family and bring us to Boston. I could not have managed the trip alone. Anna, at three and a half, was quiet and cooperative, but Louisa, not quite two, had to be watched every minute. She was unusually curious, a bundle of mischievous energy. More than once on our way to Boston my husband remarked: "I must remember to write that down in the record. How quick she is at devising ways and means to attain her purpose!" I smiled, thinking that *I* should be the one to write the record.

We talked of other things, too, while the children napped, their heads in our laps. The Germantown years had not turned out as we had hoped. But in one respect my husband had benefited greatly, and I was glad to have been able to encourage him. When we left Boston, he was not a widely-read man, though he was well-read in his own field. He had never had a chance to pursue formal studies beyond a few years in a country school. His reading had been haphazard. Now, after three years of organized reading and study, he was on firmer ground. "I will no longer feel inferior in a literary circle of college men," he told me. "Thanks to the guidance of Mr. Russell and Dr. Channing, I am now well grounded in literature."

After the low-lying country around Germantown, Boston, the city on the hill, looked especially good to me. My spirits rose to see the familiar old landmarks again, and the stately houses on Beacon Hill. Trees in their September coloring set off the city like a jewel. Surely Boston was the place where we belonged. Hadn't my husband often said that no city in the country was more mentally alive?

We stayed in a boardinghouse for a few weeks, then found a house on Front Street, not far from Boston Common. Mr. Alcott was already far along with his plans for the new school and was searching for the right location. Taking care of two lively girls meant full and busy days for me. I quickly formed the habit of taking them to the Common where Louisa could use up some of her energy running around and tumbling on the grass.

Maria Child often dropped by to have a chat with me. Far from being subdued by the opposition of many of her old readers, Maria had pursued her writing crusade against race prejudice with even more energy. Her new book, a collection of antislavery pieces, had just been published. "I have more time now to keep writing and working for the cause," she told me wryly. "I have no children's magazine left to edit, no novels to write, for I have lost my audience. But my present work brings in very little money, Abba. With David involved in the antislavery movement too, we have to watch our expenses most carefully."

I admired Maria profoundly. In some ways our lives ran parallel. Like Maria, I had married a man who was an idealist rather than a money-maker. And like Maria I had no ambition to be either wealthy or socially prominent.

Meanwhile, plans for the school progressed. Mr. Alcott had brought along journals and other writings of his boys and girls in the Germantown school, and they made an impressive record. He had a way of drawing out hidden abilities in children. Miss Elizabeth Peabody found these Germantown records exciting reading. Already she had been a great help to my husband in finding pupils and helping to organize the school. An experienced teacher herself, she knew the school situation in Boston better than anyone else. She was about thirty years old at the time, and was well known among the elite of Boston.

My husband felt that Miss Peabody's encouragement was all he needed to start a successful school. I felt otherwise. I doubted if the well-to-do of Boston would send their children to a school without more book-learning than Mr. Alcott proposed to offer. "You need an assistant," I told him. "An assistant with a sound educational background who can teach Latin and geography and arithmetic."

"Perhaps I do," he agreed. "But . . ."

It was the "but" that bothered me, too. How could we possibly afford to pay the kind of assistant he needed after furnishing the kind of school he thought he ought to have?

The predicament was solved when Miss Peabody offered her services as part-time assistant for the small sum of one hundred dollars a quarter. My husband and I were elated. "Once the school gets started, I am sure we can pay her more," he told me magnanimously.

Mr. Alcott found impressive quarters for three hundred dollars a year on the top floor of the Masonic Temple building on Tremont Street, facing the Common. And he spared no expense in refitting the rooms and decorating them with "appropriate emblems of intellectual and spiritual life," as he expressed it. Convinced that children learned more readily in a place of beauty and inspiration, he felt that elegant furnishings were a necessity. Miss Peabody helped him shop for furniture and statuary. I held my breath, concerned about going so heavily in debt for colored carpets, made-to-order desks for the children, a great pulpitlike desk for the master, busts of philosophers, and works of art. But I had to admit that the great room, really an auditorium, looked handsome when the school opened. Light streamed in through the arched Gothic windows, and the place was pervaded with the atmosphere of serenity and beauty that meant so much to my husband.

Before September was over, Temple School opened with thirty boys and girls between the ages of three and twelve, from some of the finest families in Boston. Our Louisa was too young to attend, but Anna became an eager pupil, the youngest in the school.

Mr. Alcott believed in cultivating the ears of his pupils through music and their voices through singing, and so I was able to be of assistance to him. I played the melodeon and led the school in singing. But I had to find someone to take charge of Louisa during the time I was at school. Trying to keep her from disrupting the classroom would have meant no time for music.

The fame of Temple School spread quickly and visitors came from far and near. I often noted their surprise at the beauty that surrounded the children and the quiet Mr. Alcott maintained in the schoolroom. He was ever a gentleman, and his politeness and good manners had a surprising effect on the children. They seemed to sense that he loved and respected them, that he thought them wiser than most adults realized or appreciated. He had a delightful way of getting pupils so much interested in their projects and discussions they forgot they were in school. Children were individuals, he always said, and drawing out their innate wisdom was one of the purposes of the school.

Visitors would sometimes ask Mr. Alcott how he maintained order in his classes. He would reply that he used no one method. When he first began teaching, he thought no punishment was needed or desirable. But he discovered that reasoning with a naughty child did not always work. So sometimes he would have to call a child into an anteroom and tell him to hold out his hand for punishment.

At other times he would have the children choose a superintendent from among them each day to decide on any punishments, which my husband would carry out faithfully. Sometimes Mr. Alcott even went so far as to have the child strike him, instead of striking the child. "In that way," he explained, "the wrongdoer realizes that his misconduct hurts not only himself but others."

When visitors questioned Mr. Alcott about his method of teaching, he was always glad to tell them how he tried to teach his pupils from within instead of cramming facts into them and forcing them to memorize things. He encouraged them to keep journals of their thoughts as well as their activities.

So highly developed was Mr. Alcott's art of conversation that he succeeded in getting amazing replies and comments in his talks with children. Before the first quarter was over, Miss Peabody was saying that someone ought to be recording the "immortal words" of these conversations. She thought them too beautiful and precious to lose. In the end she herself began taking notes on the talks, writing as fast as she could, until her fingers cramped. Then in the evening she would go over her notes, making them legible. I was appalled when I realized how many hours a day she was devoting to Temple School. Yet how, I asked myself, could we pay her even the small salary agreed upon?

In the evening Bronson often read to me from the transcript of the day before while I sat with my sewing basket. One winter night he seemed particularly pleased as he sat down with Miss Peabody's pages. "That Josiah Quincy!" he exclaimed. "Only six years old, and you should hear him, Abba. Of course, coming from such a prominent family, he has advantages. But he is a constant surprise and delight to me."

"He is the one who stammers a little?"

"Yes, but it doesn't affect his flow of ideas. In fact, my theory is that he stammers because his ideas tumble out so fast. His great fault is that he wants to talk too much. For the sake of the other children I feel I must restrain him."

"What was it this time?" I asked, looking up from my mending.

"We were talking about worship, and Josiah had some inspired thoughts about it. Listen to the transcript." He began to read:

"Josiah: Spirit worships Spirit. Clay worships Clay.
. . . Mr. Alcott, we think too much about clay. We
should think of Spirit . . . I should think a mother
now would love her baby's Spirit; and suppose it
should die, that is only the Spirit bursting away out
of the Body. It is alive; it is perfectly happy. I really
do not know why people mourn when their friends
die. I should think it would be a matter of rejoicing.
For instance: now, if we should go out into the street
and find a box—an old dusty box—and should put into
it some very fine pearls, and by and by the box should
grow old and break, why, we should not even think
about the box; but if the pearls were safe, we should
think of them and nothing else. So it is with the Soul
and Body. I cannot see why people mourn for bodies."

I had stopped my sewing to listen. Little Josiah
Quincy seemed wise beyond belief. "Did Miss Peabody take down his exact words? Without adding wisdom of her own?"

"The exact words of the conversation, so far as her
pencil was able to keep up with it. I assure you, Abba,
she had no time to pause and think."

"You do indeed know how to draw the children
out," I said, smiling admiringly at the handsome
schoolmaster sitting opposite me. "I doubt if anything
like this has been done before."

One day after Miss Peabody and my husband had
gone over some of the transcripts, they simultaneously

37

saw the possibility of a book in them, a book on the record of an unusual school. I expressed my unqualified enthusiasm when Mr. Alcott came home and talked it over with me.

Again the work fell on the competent and willing shoulders of Elizabeth Peabody. I knew that she did not agree with all of Bronson Alcott's ideas, but I was confident that her editing would be both fair and judicious. This proved to be the case. As Recorder she put down my husband's theories, and carefully organized the material.

The manuscript was published late that summer under the title *Record of a School*. We were all tremendously pleased and excited about it and hopeful that public reaction would be favorable.

Our hopes were justified. *Record of a School* soon attracted a great deal of attention in educational circles not only in the United States, but in England and other countries as well. "Now you are going to get the recognition you deserve," I told my husband joyously.

The school was doing well, and attracting more and more attention and visitors, when our third child was born on the 24th of June, 1835. It turned out to be another girl. I had hoped it would be a boy, and so had my husband, I am sure, although he had never said so. But the new blonde daughter quickly captured our hearts. Anna and Louisa were entranced. Anna, gentle and motherly, could be depended upon to watch over her little sister. Louisa, I soon found, was too unpredictable to be trusted. In a fit of impatience she would shake the baby roughly, or threaten her with a toy, or abandon her altogether.

We named our new little girl Elizabeth, after Elizabeth Peabody, to show our hard-working friend the great esteem in which we held her.

I had not been feeling too well before the birth of Elizabeth, and afterward it took me some time to regain my strength. I felt harassed. With three children to look after, a household to manage, clothes to keep in repair, social activities to attend to in connection with the school, and my duties there, I found little time for rest and reading. Reading had always been an important part of my life, and I missed it. Fortunately Mr. Alcott came to my rescue. He read aloud to me whenever possible, and conversation with him was always a delight. Besides, he took over some of the care of the children, dressing Anna and Louisa in the morning while I tended to baby Elizabeth. From nine till one, Anna was with him at school. And in the afternoon, after their naps, he usually had the two older children with him in his study, Miss Peabody taking charge of the afternoon classes at the school.

Even so, there was little time for me to be active in movements that interested me. My brother Sam and my cousin Samuel Sewall were becoming more and more involved in antislavery work. My husband had joined them in supporting William Lloyd Garrison and his *Liberator*. I was as avid an antislavery crusader

39

as any of them, but for the most part I had to rely on them and on my friend Maria Child to keep me informed of what was happening "on the inside" in the movement.

In October our fiery friend Mr. Garrison was mobbed at a meeting of the Boston Female Anti-Slavery Society which he had been invited to address. A crowd dragged him through the streets with a rope around his neck, until the Mayor intervened and had him taken to jail for safety. Feeling was running high against those advocating freedom for the slaves. Boston merchants might agree that morally slavery was wrong, but business between the North and South had become adjusted to it, and business, of course, came first.

The mobbing of Mr. Garrison came on a day my husband returned from his first visit of several days with Mr. Ralph Waldo Emerson in Concord. The two men had met that summer and were immediately attracted to each other. Mr. Alcott was telling me in stirring words of his memorable visit, describing the fall beauties of Concord village with flaming maples along the wide streets, and exclaiming, "Never have I found a man with whose mind I felt more sympathy . . . never have I been so in communion with another man's spirit," when a friend came to the door with the news of Mr. Garrison's narrow escape from the mob.

We visited Mr. Garrison in jail that evening. He was in high spirits despite his narrow escape from being tarred and feathered, more eager than ever to press ahead against slavery. While we were there John Greenleaf Whittier, whose poems Mr. Garrison had published on more than one occasion, came to pay his respects. Others came, too, and talk was lively. "Tonight," Mr. Garrison told us, "I shall decorate my cell with antislavery inscriptions in prose and verse, as I did when they jailed me in Baltimore." With men of such courage working against slavery, I thought, the crusade cannot help but succeed.

My husband's decision to become a vegetarian about this time rather distressed me. I did not agree with him that a diet without animal products was to be preferred to a mixed diet, and I could not help being concerned about his health. He ate so sparingly and, it seemed to me, so monotonously . . . mostly whole grain bread and apples . . . I wondered how he could keep up his energy. I was glad that he carried his theories of individualism from the classroom to the home and did not try to force his vegetarianism on the rest of us.

He assured me that the more abstemious he was, the clearer his mind seemed to be. "I will gladly do anything," he told me, "to be able to look Truth full in the face. If this means eating sparingly, it is what I shall do with pleasure and expectation." In view of his worthy aim, I could hardly urge him to change his mind.

That fall Louisa was three years old and her father

thirty-six. I conspired with Elizabeth Peabody and some of the older pupils to hold a surprise party at the school. I composed a little ode and set it to music for the children to sing. We made a crown of flowers for Louisa's head and stood her on the table to pass out a little cake to each child as he went by.

Louisa, gay and high-spirited, behaved like a model hostess until she came to the last of the cakes. I was horrified to see that we had miscounted and were one short. Before her stood the last child waiting for his cake. Louisa clutched it to herself. I knew the time had come for me to intervene, even though she was the birthday child. "Louy," I said softly, "it is always better to give away the nice things. I know you don't want the little boy to go without his cake."

Louisa looked at me, her lip trembling. I fully expected her to have a tantrum. But for once she fooled me. Reluctantly she opened her hand. Slowly she gave the cake to the waiting child. With a flood of affection and admiration I pressed her to me.

CHAPTER 5

IN THE SPRING OF '36 we asked Miss Peabody to come live with us in our home on Front Street. We felt guilty that we had been unable to pay her. Even though the school prospered, there were always so many prior expenses, we had nothing left by the time we came to Miss Peabody. By giving her a bright, well-furnished room and having her take her meals with us, we hoped to make up a little for all her devoted work at the school. She enjoyed our girls, particularly her namesake Elizabeth with whom she liked to play a little every day. I was hopeful that the arrangement would be a happy one for all of us.

Miss Peabody at this time was engrossed in compiling a second book, as a sequel to *Record of a School*. This was to be called *Conversations with Children on the Gospels.* Many a night our conscientious roomer burned the midnight oil as she worked over the notes she had taken of my husband's conversations with his pupils.

When, in June, she had to go to Lowell for some weeks to care for a sick friend, her younger sister Sophia took her place, and continued recording the conversations. Sophia Peabody was an artist, a gentle soul, in not very robust health. I feared she might overdo. But she handled the work very well, and we were pleased with her.

Mr. Alcott had begun a new series of Conversations on the Bible some months before. They were held on Sunday mornings, and pupils came with their parents. I tried taking Louisa to one of the meetings and she was so fascinated by the stories she forgot to get into mischief. In the group were orthodox Sunday School teachers. I could see amazement, indeed horror, written on their faces when Mr. Alcott spoke of Jesus as if he were a *man*, a truly exceptional man, a son of God, yet still a man. They were horrified, too, when he spoke of the Christian religion as only one of several "respectable" religions. I feared he was treading on forbidden ground.

When my husband started Temple School and put his innovations into effect, Boston was prosperous and open to new ideas. People thought well of him and the newspapers praised him. But before two years passed, Boston began to feel the effects of a depression. Good times changed to bad. Banks failed. People began to be afraid of new ideas. Outspoken criticism of Mr. Alcott's new methods of teaching began to circulate.

Critics asked why he had set himself up against the time-honored methods of storing young minds with useful facts. What sense was there, they asked, in carrying on conversations with children to draw out the truth that was in them? As if there could be anything in their minds before they were stored with facts.

One June day, in the second year of the school, Mr. Ralph Waldo Emerson climbed the stairs in the tower of the Masonic Temple to listen to a conversation on the Gospel of St. John. He was then in his early thirties, some three years younger than my husband. Tall, slender, and slightly stooped, he stepped lightly into the room and seated himself beside Mr. Alcott, as the pupils were quietly arranging their chairs in a semicircle in front of him. I had just finished leading the school in music and regretted that I could not wait to listen to the conversation.

When my husband came home I was full of questions. "What did Mr. Emerson think? Did the conversation go off well? Did little Josiah Quincy have anything to say?"

My husband smiled as he answered. "Mr. Emerson remarked afterward that he felt strongly that to truth there is no age or season."

"Just what you have always said."

"Josiah made a deep impression on him. He could not believe that the child was not yet seven. 'When a child perceives truth he is no more a child,' was Mr. Emerson's comment."

Mr. Emerson's approval strengthened my husband's desire to go ahead quickly with the book. But as work on the transcript progressed, I could sense a widening difference of opinion between Bronson Alcott and Elizabeth Peabody. True, she was a great admirer of his. Yet she feared that the school and everyone connected with it would suffer if all the conversations, particularly those that dealt with birth, were printed exactly as they had taken place.

"You will only antagonize people," she warned Mr. Alcott. "Clergymen will resent your invasion of their field, and educators even now object to your methods of teaching. Besides, what will socially proper mothers in their Boston parlors say when they see in black and white that you discuss the mystery of birth with a mixed group of boys and girls?"

We both tried to reassure Miss Peabody by pointing out that when people had a chance to read the conversations for themselves, they would see how really inspired and poetic some of the children's answers had been.

"Birth is like rain," one child had said. "It comes from heaven."

"Birth is like the rising light of the sun," said another. "The setting is death."

A third said, "God's wind came upon the ocean of life, and washed up the waters a little into a channel, and that is birth. They run up farther, and that is living."

Others thought that angels might bring babies as a great surprise to their mothers.

How, I wondered, could anyone be embarrassed or shocked by Mr. Alcott's gentle explanation that when a mother is going to have a child, she gives up her body to God, and he works upon it in a mysterious way, "and with her aid, brings forth the child's spirit in a little body of its own."

Rather than be connected with the school when *Conversations on the Gospels* appeared in print, Miss Peabody resigned her post late in the summer. She wrote a letter explaining her feelings in detail. I could quite understand her point of view, yet I felt a little impatient with Miss Peabody, I must confess, for bowing to the imagined whims of public opinion.

For a while after Elizabeth Peabody withdrew, Margaret Fuller assisted at the school. She had an intellectual background that awed me. Her father had seen to it that she learned Latin as soon as she could speak. By the time she was fifteen she knew French, Greek, and Italian, played the piano and sang, and was well-read in philosophy. Now at twenty-six, Margaret was a woman of many accomplishments, and so good a teacher that I was sorry when we were unable to entice her to stay longer than a few weeks.

Meanwhile Mr. Alcott found a source of inspiration that lifted him above his troubles at the school. Early in September a gathering of congenial men, among them Mr. Emerson, held a meeting at the home of the Reverend Mr. George Ripley. The group was interested in discussing new ideas, and Mr. Emerson's new book *Nature* became their first textbook, so to speak. Never have I seen my husband more stimulated than when he came home from that meeting. Talk, especially talk about new ideas, was more important to him than almost anything else. "I have asked them to come to our house for the next meeting," he told me. "It will be early in October."

Seven distinguished clergymen and scholars, including Mr. Emerson, were there in addition to my husband at the second meeting of what outsiders soon began to call the Transcendental Club. Mr. Alcott was in his element. The topic was "American Genius," and he felt he knew what hindered the development of genius in America: we were still too subservient to Europe in scholarship, literature, art, music. We needed to strike out for ourselves and have confidence in our ability to create our own culture.

After much spirited discussion, the meeting broke up with the understanding that the members would meet again whenever possible. Sometimes meetings were held in our home, or in the homes of other Boston members, but most often in Concord, about twenty miles away, at the home of Mr. Emerson. Mr.

Henry Thoreau of Concord soon became a member, and in time Elizabeth Peabody and Margaret Fuller were invited to join.

In spite of Miss Peabody's warnings, Mr. Alcott went ahead with the publication of *Conversations on the Gospels*. The first volume came out three days before Christmas, 1836 and the second volume followed a few weeks later. We had to add almost eight hundred dollars to our debt to bring out the books, but, of course, we hoped that sales would eventually more than make up for it. Eagerly we looked forward to notices in the Boston papers, confident that they would be favorable.

How bitter was our disappointment! How unnerving our ordeal! From the first, most newspaper commentators greeted *Conversations* with a storm of protest. "We cannot repress our indignation . . ." cried one paper. "More indecent and obscene than any other book," said another. "Absurd." "Blasphemous." Vilifications poured down on my poor husband's head from the aroused press unwilling to accept his new ideas in education.

More than ever now I realized what Maria must have gone through after the publication of *Appeal*, when abuse and defamation from the defenders of slavery engulfed her. I was even afraid to have Mr. Alcott walk the streets of Boston alone. Popular feeling against him ran so high that children hooted at him and mob violence was in the air—just such violence as our friend Mr. Garrison had endured, but for a different reason.

Comforting letters came, too, of course, but they were unable to offset the flood of abuse. Josiah Quincy's mother wrote in praise of Mr. Alcott's school and his teaching methods. Orestes Brownson, preacher and writer, wrote a long article, "Alcott on Human Culture," for the *Boston Quarterly Review*. No man in the country so well understood the art of education, Mr. Brownson said. "He will never sacrifice what he holds as truth, virtue, manhood, independence, to popular opinion . . ." How true, how true, yet how gruelling when popular opinion was so overwhelmingly against him.

Mr. Emerson wrote letters to the papers in defense of Mr. Alcott, and in addition a personal letter to my husband in which he said he hated to see all the little dogs barking at him. "You are so deeply grounded in God," he wrote, "that I shall not fear for you any loss of faith in your ends by opposition."

Even Elizabeth Peabody, loyal in spite of everything, wrote a defense of Temple School and its master. And her sister Sophia sent a consoling letter, saying that she thought the conversations about birth should have been received with reverence and thanks. She felt her own mind had been elevated by them. "New ideas," she commented, "are always received with consternation"—the truth of which Mr. Alcott and I were learning all too well.

Margaret Fuller also rose to my husband's defense. Miss Fuller called Mr. Alcott "a true and noble man, a philanthropist, a philosopher worthy of the glorious days of ancient Greece."

But the defamers overwhelmingly outnumbered the defenders. The school was doomed. That spring Mr. Alcott suffered the agony of seeing it go completely to pieces. Only ten pupils remained. I suffered doubly —through his suffering and my own grievous disappointment in the fate of the school, and through my inability to see what would become of us if my husband had to give up teaching.

The beautiful furnishings had to be stripped from the schoolroom and auctioned off to pay part of our debts. It tore my heart to hear him say, "My schoolroom! My beautiful schoolroom!" as one carefully chosen object after another came down. Yet when I railed against the fate that was dealing so harshly with us, he reasoned with me and tried to console me as if I were the injured one, not he. His patient endurance of injustice and ignorance staggered me.

In addition to dismantling the schoolroom, my husband had to part with many of his beloved books. He had no choice but to move his school from the spacious auditorium to the dark and stuffy basement of the Temple. And we could no longer afford to live in our Front Street home but had to move to a cheaper house in the south end of Boston.

My good friend Maria Child was having troubles

of her own at this time, and she often came knocking at my door for companionship. Her husband had gone abroad to make a time-consuming study of sugar production. He and Mr. Garrison sought to prove that beet sugar grown in the northern states without slave labor could compete with cane sugar grown in the south with slave labor. Maria was as devoted to her husband as I was to mine, and the separation of many months was hard on her. During the first year Mr. Child was gone, the girls and I were often able to ease her loneliness, but the next year, as Temple School fell to pieces, I turned to her for consolation more often than she turned to me.

As blow after blow fell, my husband suffered in silence. He was not ill in any way that a doctor could remedy; he was simply heartbroken. He steeled himself against criticism, insult and abuse, and yet was torn apart inside. I realized how utterly discouraged he felt when he could not even bring himself to write in his Journal for several months. I knew, though, that he would never compromise his ideals to get back into public favor.

I would have been glad to take up some kind of work to bring in an income to save us from further financial troubles. But what work could I get? And how could I leave my three small daughters? Resignedly I wrote to my brother Sam: "I sometimes think extreme poverty awaits us."

At the year-end some unknown friend sent Mr. Alcott a purse of a hundred dollars. Instead of dancing for joy, as I did with baby Elizabeth in my arms and Anna and Louisa cavorting beside me, my husband stood quietly blinking the mist from his eyes. He was more touched by this evidence of appreciation and friendship than he was elated by the windfall of needed dollars.

CHAPTER 6

IN THE SPRING AND SUMMER after Temple School fell to pieces, several things combined to pull Mr. Alcott out of his depression. The first happened quite inadvertently. Bright and early one Sunday morning I asked him if he would kindly take Anna and Louisa to the Common for some exercise. We lived farther from it now that we had moved, and the children were unable to go so often. Anna was six that summer and Louisa going on five. "It is such a wonderful morning," I pointed out. "And the girls mind you so well. I'm sure you will find them no burden, and really, Louisa must have an outlet for her energy or she will drive me to distraction."

He looked at me solemnly, as if appraising my nearness to distraction, then reluctantly consented to go.

Some time later he returned, holding sedate Anna by one hand and bedraggled, mud-stained Louisa by the other. "Whatever happened!" I cried, ready to scold Louisa for ruining her clean dress. But I caught myself. Did I detect something of the old lightness in her father's step? Was there not a hint of new life in his face?

"Louisa fell into the frog pond at the deep end," my husband said. "I am afraid I was too occupied with my thoughts, Abba, to watch her as I should have. I thought I heard a splash and a cry . . . then Anna came running and calling for me."

"Poor little Louy!" I leaned down and put my arms around her. "Are you quite all right? Did it hurt? Mother will wash the dress and make it pretty again."

"She might well have drowned," my husband was saying. "But a colored boy pulled her out."

"A colored boy? And what was his name? If only you had brought him home with you so I could thank him, too!"

"He just *went*," Anna said. "After we shook the water out of Louy, we couldn't find him."

I looked questioningly at my husband.

"Anna is right. The boy vanished before I could even thank him." His blue eyes had some of their old spark. "But the episode taught me some things I had been forgetting, Abba . . . about love, and gratitude. What does the temporary failure of a school matter when we have our Lu safe, and our Anna, and Elizabeth, and each other?"

That was the beginning of his cure. A week or two later Brother Sam suggested that he come for a visit to Scituate, south of Boston, where he was then preaching. "You need a complete change," he wrote. "The sea breezes will invigorate you."

I packed my husband's bag, and he went. He came home refreshed and renewed. But it took Mr. Emerson to effect the final cure. "Come out here instantly to spend a fortnight with me," he wrote. It was at a time when Mr. Emerson was working on "The American Scholar," a Phi Beta Kappa Day address. My husband talked over parts of the address with him and later heard him deliver it at Harvard.

Our little girls helped fill the hole in my life while I waited hopefully for Mr. Alcott to be freed from his depression and return ready to face the future with his old buoyancy. Louisa kept me busy. I had to have her on my mind continually, for she liked to run away, just as I had done at her age. The year before she had wandered off and got lost, finally going to sleep in a doorway, snuggled next to a big dog. The town crier found her there well after dark, while her anxious parents were going up one street and down the next looking for her. Before she was five, she was an expert at rolling her hoop and running and jumping on the grass of the Common. She should have been born a boy, I often thought, wondering if my husband had made the same observation in his voluminous records.

Little Lizzie, as we affectionately called Elizabeth, was two years old that summer, light-haired and happy. Even at that age she showed an interest in the tales I told the older girls about their Grandfather May and their Grandmother Sewall and long-ago Chief Justice Sewall. I played with the children a great deal, read to them, walked with them, and longed for the day when their father would again feel like romping with them.

Mr. Alcott came home from Concord exhilarated. He told me how much it had meant to him to walk with his congenial companion through the countryside. And he told me about "The American Scholar." "One thing I can't get out of my mind, Abba. In his paper Mr. Emerson was addressing scholars. Yet he pointed out that there is virtue in the hoe and spade, for learned as well as for unlearned hands." He spread his strong, competent hands before me. "I have been thinking the same thing for a long time. My hands fit well on the handle of a hoe or spade, after my boyhood experience on my father's farm. And I often have a craving to smell the good earth. If I could but have a garden to cultivate and an orchard to prune!"

I nodded. "A garden and an orchard would be a great help. But where . . . how . . . ?" The section of Boston where we lived and no space for gardens and orchards.

Those were troubled days. Charges were still being hurled against Mr. Alcott, one of them being that he was a ringleader of the Transcendentalists in Boston. And was theirs not a dangerous movement intent on undermining religion and society? The charge was ridiculous, of course. There was no real leader of the movement, and the Transcendentalists were quite harmless. They had an optimistic faith in human nature, which I found very easy to accept. They did not agree with the common belief that our minds are a blank when we are born. Instead they believed that we are born with an inner light to guide us, an intuition that tells us what is right and what is wrong.

God is within us, said the Transcendentalists, for God is everywhere, in every single thing in the universe and in every one of us without exception. We feel His Presence and need not gain all our knowledge of Him through books and teachers. It was natural for my husband to believe this. As a boy on the ridge of a lonely hill near his farm home, he had often felt the Presence and been aware of the mystery and wonder of it.

Mr. Emerson continued to be the bright light in those dark times. He would come to Boston to lecture, to visit the art galleries, and to read in the Athenaeum library. There my husband would join him and they would go to one of the private rooms for a good talk together. Or Mr. Emerson would drop in at our house to discuss articles in the English magazines and the need for an American publication to voice the ideas of the new age.

Often after Mr. Emerson left, my husband would express his great delight in their friendship. He considered Emerson the only man he knew who possessed real creative genius, and thought his influence greater than that of any other man. "I wish I might go around teaching and preaching in the nearby towns and villages, Abba . . . something in the way Mr. Emerson lectures from town to town. Not formal lectures, though. I would like to teach as Socrates did, through dialogue and conversation to small groups."

"In the meantime we must live," I pointed out.

To this my dear impractical husband would sigh and say, "I am an Idea without hands, eager to do some service for the soul. But the age has no place for me." Or he would smile and assure me with the confidence of a child: "I have faith that if I can find a way to express the spirit that fills me, our worldly needs will take care of themselves."

In the fall Mr. Alcott faced the task of trying to start another school. He fitted out a schoolroom in our new home on Beech Street and lined up fifteen pupils. Soon Mr. Russell of Germantown days came with his young son to live with us, and our house was full of high talk. Whatever discouragement my husband still felt about the failure of his Temple school, he buried in uplifting conversation with Mr. Russell.

Our friend favored the idea of Conversations in nearby towns, and my husband tried them out, holding some in our own home as well. The response was good, but the money-return pathetically small.

Meanwhile my good friend Maria Child and her husband were having an even harder time than we were. David Child had come back from his sugar-beet research in Europe in the spring. There seemed to be no place for him in Boston, and he and Maria were without money or work for several months. Finally Maria's father offered to buy them a farm in western Massachusetts where they could experiment with sugar beets, on condition they permit him to live with them. The farm was run-down, the house badly neglected, and Maria's father so opinionated he was impossible to live with.

Maria snatched time to write me occasionally, telling me of the unending farm work and the hard physical labor from three or four o'clock in the morning until late at night. We Alcotts, for all our straitened circumstances, were better off. I tried to be cheerful and encouraging in writing to Maria, and did my best to keep her up to date on abolitionist news, books, mutual friends, and other things I knew she must be missing.

Soon after the little Beech Street school was opened, a bit of encouragement came to us from England. A Mr. Greaves of London, an educator, wrote that he found *Conversations on the Gospels* an invaluable work. He ordered twelve copies, and also requested some copies of the second edition of *Record of a School*. My husband was overjoyed to have this recognition from such an unexpected source. He answered Mr. Greaves immediately, beginning a voluminous and stimulating interchange of ideas with him.

Nevertheless, the year 1839 was a despairing one for us. Though the active vilification brought about by the publication of *Conversations* had died down in Boston, the aftereffects remained. We had little money though my husband worked hard. He always helped me with the children and with the heavy housework. In cold weather he sawed and split the wood to feed our fires, for it was cheaper to buy logs than cord wood. From nine to twelve in the morning and from three to five in the afternoon he taught in his school. Three or four evenings a week he carried on Conversations, and, of course, he had to be reading and studying continually in preparation. Besides, he kept a detailed journal of his thoughts and activities. I often marveled that a man could put in so many hours a day for so little return.

In April came a tragedy of quite a different sort. A son was born to us at last, but he died before he had really begun to live.

I could not hold back a flood of tears. A son . . . and snatched from us so quickly! My husband, his own eyes glistening, consoled me. "Abba, remember what Josiah Quincy said that we thought was such a revelation? 'Suppose a mother's baby should die,' he said. 'That is only the Spirit bursting away out of the body. It is alive; it is perfectly happy.' At the time I thought everything he said was true, and I still think so, though we miss the presence of our little son."

Anna and Louisa found it hard to understand about their little brother, whom we laid away in my father's lot in the old burial-ground on the Common. Months later I heard them speaking of him tenderly as they played with their dolls. "But is he happy?" Louisa asked. Anna assured her that he was. I blinked back my tears and quietly went about my work.

One Saturday, as an antidote to my troubles, one of of my friends urged me to go as her guest to one of Margaret Fuller's Conversations. I needed no urging. I was curious to see Elizabeth Peabody's new book-shop in West Street where Margaret's Conversations were held. Transcendentalists and other "minds" con-gregated there in the afternoons, intent on high-minded talk.

It seemed to me that half the feminine "minds" of Boston were there for Margaret's noon Conversation. She talked about Life, and we were all inspired to join her in trying to fathom what it really was. And, at least for the time being, under the stimulation of the ideas bandied about, it seemed that we did get some light on this great mystery. I parted from my friend with a light heart, and hurried home to share the high points of the afternoon with Mr. Alcott.

My husband continued to have hard luck with his school teaching. In June he admitted Susan Robinson, a Negro child, to the little Beech Street School. Feeling as we did on the slavery question, it was only natural for him to do this without considering the consequences Almost at once angry white parents demanded Susan's dismissal and made quite a fuss about it. Mr. Alcott, of course, would not give in, even when child after child was withdrawn from the school. Finally only our own children, Susan Robinson, and William Russell's son were left.

All Boston heard about it, although the school had been obscure enough for months. A Negro child in Bronson Alcott's school! What would the man do next? My memory flew back to the trouble Prudence Crandall had in Connecticut when she admitted Negro pupils. Boston was just as closed-minded. The school came to an abrupt end.

In dismay I looked toward the future. Here we were, deeply in debt, with three small girls, and no means of earning a living. Where were we to turn? Brother Sam, dear, good, dependable Sam saved the summer for us by suggesting that we come to Scituate at his expense. It gave us all a new hold on life.

There at the seashore, Mr. Alcott taught the children their morning lessons in the garden where he could call their attention to the wonders of nature. Afterwards, the girls and their three May cousins spent carefree hours racing along the shore, wading, swimming, and watching the waves break and the gulls wheel.

Every day we combed the beach for surprises

washed up by the waves during the night—shells and driftwood, fishermen's floats, strange pods and weeds, and bits of worn glass. We took turns making up stories about the treasures we found. I thought Louisa showed great talent in dramatizing her stories, and I found myself looking forward to what she would think of next.

Mr. Alcott had some success with his Conversations that summer, holding them at intervals in nearby towns. They built up his confidence, which was as important at that point as building up our pocketbook.

On Sundays we attended services at Sam's church. Often there was a picnic afterward in a shady grove, where we ate prodigiously, and talked, and laughed, and sang hymns. The girls had never known such a summer.

With the coming of September, the summer people began to close their houses and move back to the city. It was time for us to think of returning to Boston. Reluctantly we left, knowing that Scituate was a little corner of paradise none of us would ever forget.

CHAPTER 7

BACK IN BOSTON, pressure increased for us to make a decision about the future. We Alcotts seemed to be living in two worlds. One was a world where we could completely forget our worries for hours at a time—when friends gathered in the parlor of our little house for high talk. Mr. Emerson came, and Dr. Channing, and Margaret Fuller, and Theodore Parker and others, with my husband leading the conversation more often than not. I was not the only one who found him a magnetic conversationalist. In the world of ideas Bronson Alcott was sought after, appreciated, and listened to with respect.

The other world engulfed us at every meal, at the receipt of every bill, and at the sight of our clothes getting threadbare and shiny. "High thinking and plain living," yes. But how long could it continue?

One morning as if in answer, my husband handed me a slip of paper with some figures on it. "I don't see how we can go on like this much longer," he said.

I glanced at the figures. They told the pitiful story of what had happened to his earnings from teaching, beginning with the opening of Temple School five years before. From a high of $1794 for his best year, his income from teaching had shrunk to a low of $343 for the year just passed.

"Besides," he continued, determined at last to face the worst, "I am deeply in debt, as you know only too well. I must owe nearly six thousand dollars, and I don't see how I can ever repay it."

I nodded. Something had to be done soon, and we both knew it. We could not keep coasting along, accepting help from my relatives and going further into debt. Yet what could my husband do? Work in a factory was to be had, but he was temperamentally unfitted for it and I was unwilling for him to try it. If only we had a piece of land where he could grow vegetables and fruit to keep us alive!

"There must be *something* I am fitted for," my husband murmured. A note of hope crept into his voice as he continued. "A philosopher, living a philosopher's life! I could really dedicate myself to that. And I could keep on with the Conversations, too. They bring out a lively response in most groups."

My heart went out to him. Here he was, almost

forty, and proposing so impractical a plan. The glow was back in his blue eyes, the glow I had missed for so long, and it had been brought back by the mere thought of living a philosopher's life. How could I remind him that the little groups of twenty or thirty men and women who took part in his stimulating parlor Conversations paid him very little indeed for an evening's time?

I was afraid it would crush him if I vetoed the plan outright, so I only ventured to ask, "But will the earnings of a philosopher support a family, do you think?"

He came across the room with his old springing step and bent down to take my hands in his. "Oh, Abba, let us try not to look at this with sensible eyes. A purpose like mine must bear fruit in some kind of living for us. We don't have to work out the arithmetic beforehand, do we?" And so we let the arithmetic take care of itself in making our plans.

A few weeks later Mr. Alcott came home from one of his periodic visits with Mr. Emerson in Concord. "We had some wonderful talks," he said. "Among other things we discussed my plight from all angles. It is obvious I can never teach again in Boston. Mr. Emerson suggests that we move to Concord, where living will be cheaper. We will be warmly welcomed there, and perhaps we may be able to take in some children as pupils and boarders. I can have a garden, and surely find other work to do with my hands. What do you say, my dear?"

Full of hope, I grasped at the suggestion. "Yes," I said. "Yes." In a country village my husband would have a chance to combine gardening with the life of a philosopher.

We were lucky to be able to rent the small but pleasant Hosmer cottage on the outskirts of Concord, about a mile from the Emersons. With the cottage went an acre of ground for a garden. The rent was only fifty dollars a year, and Mr. Emerson, understanding friend that he was, offered to pay it. My husband was eager to sink his roots into the soil, to cultivate a large garden for our own use, and to hire out as a day laborer on nearby farms.

"We go to Concord for another experiment in the art of living," I wrote my brother Sam with hopeful anticipation at the time of our moving in early April, 1840. I told him that the sale of Mr. Alcott's schoolroom furniture and some household articles would probably pay for his garden tools and for our transportation. And I was sure that the pure country air would improve our health. I had been feeling poorly for some weeks, and was expecting another baby late in July.

Even before his garden was planted, Mr. Alcott had a great lift of spirit. A letter came from an unknown admirer in England, a Mr. Charles Lane, a friend of Mr. Greaves with whom my husband corresponded. Mr. Lane wrote the exciting news that Mr. Greaves had established a school and named it *Alcott House*.

"Alcott House!" I exclaimed. "What a tribute."

My husband gave me a pleased smile. "Mr. Lane writes that if I can manage to get to England, I will find at Alcott House a considerable group of transcendental Englishmen who have been regarding me as their master for some time. Can you believe it, Abba?"

"A prophet is not without honor save in his own country," I reminded him, almost overcome with tenderness and sympathy. But how, how could Bronson Alcott ever manage to get to England?

He patted my head as he went toward the kitchen door. "First I have other seeds to sow," he said.

The Emersons invited us—all of us—for the noon meal on Sunday shortly after we moved to Concord. We walked over in the spring sunshine, with birds singing around us and new green showing in the fields and on the hills. My husband took my hand and Elizabeth's, while Louisa and Anna skipped along beside us, and we all felt more joyous than we had for months.

I shall never forget the warmth of the Emersons' welcome, and their interest in our three girls. They had two young children of their own—Ellen just a little over a year old, and Waldo almost four. He was a beautiful boy, just such a boy as our lost son might have grown to be. Impulsively I reached out my hands to him, but he ducked behind his father's long legs. "Waldo and his father are great friends," Mrs. Emerson confided. "They speak a special language of their own. And they are so *concerned* about each other, so considerate. We have a family joke. Mr. Emerson is not too handy with tools. One day when Waldo was watching him dig in the garden, he pleaded, "I wish you would not dig your leg, Father."

Louisa, listening with both ears, giggled, and poked Anna.

I liked Mrs. Emerson. She was an intelligent, well-read woman who delighted in her family and in her husband's pleasure in his guests.

The Emersons spoke of the good school Henry Thoreau and his brother John were conducting in Concord, but, of course, we were in no position to send our girls to a private school. Besides, we had a perfectly good schoolmaster in our own family. "The Thoreau brothers are devoted to each other and work well together," Mr. Emerson said. "Henry is like you in matters of discipline, Mr. Alcott. The school is well ahead of its time."

My husband was already acquainted with young Henry Thoreau, still in his early twenties, since he was a member of the Transcendentalist group. "I wonder how long the school will last," he mused. "But perhaps Concord is different."

For us, Concord *was* different, and in a good way. Although Boston continued to have a hold on me, I was more and more glad as the weeks passed that we had left the city. After all, it was not far away nor hard to reach—only three hours by stagecoach, and coaches ran daily.

Concord was an unusually attractive village, with wide streets and shady elms and a slow-moving river. From the first the girls loved the freedom and beauty of the little town and the country around it. Anna was nine that summer, Louisa going on eight, and little Elizabeth five. With the Hosmer children next door for playmates, they spent most of the summer out-of-doors.

I sometimes worried about Louy, knowing how high-spirited she was, how almost recklessly adventuresome, but I trusted Anna to restrain her. Still Louisa often managed to get into trouble. I will never forget the day she had to be trundled home in a wheelbarrow, green in the face from chewing tobacco the fieldhands had pressed upon her. And the day she took the Hosmer boy's dare and jumped from a high beam in the barn. That time she was carried home on a board, with two sprained ankles.

By the end of June our garden was beginning to produce. And what a beautiful big garden it was. With a grateful heart I looked forward to an abundance of fresh vegetables for months to come. And in the fall we would have fruit to pick and store. My husband was getting a little work, too, now and then, helping in the fields. If we could just keep from going further into debt, I would be glad to continue to live in the utmost simplicity to the end of my days, I assured myself.

I will confess though that I was ambitious for our girls. I wanted them to have a full and happy life. Mr. Alcott, I knew, would give them an educational and cultural background that no amount of money could buy. But I wanted them never to feel poor in spirit. And I doubt that they did, even in our darkest hours.

Out of our small stores we always had enough to share with someone less fortunate than we, even if it meant giving away half of our meager dinner or parting with some of our woodpile. Ever since Louy's lesson with the cakes on her third birthday at Temple School, she had been one of the first to urge sharing our "riches" with a needy friend or family. I reassured myself that so long as the children felt that way, we could never be poor.

Always, no matter how simple or small our home, I tried to redeem it with touches of beauty here and there. I kept a high polish on our choice pieces of wedding-present furniture and the old May piano. The girls and I took turns shining the silver dish and keeping it full of short-stemmed flowers in summer and dried sprigs of weeds and seed pods in winter. I saw to it that we had attractive curtains, rescued from the barrels of discarded clothes and hangings my relatives sent periodically. And there were always flowering plants and books on open shelves. Though we often had only dark bread and apples for dinner, we always had something of homelike beauty around us to look at.

That summer the members of the Transcendental group finally put through their plan to establish a journal. My husband supplied the name. He suggested calling it *The Dial*, a name he had given to his own journals which he faithfully kept over the years. Margaret Fuller became *The Dial*'s first editor, and Mr. Emerson wrote the introductory address.

How eagerly my husband came home from Boston in July, 1840, with the first copy of *The Dial* to show me! We pored over it all evening after the children went to bed. Of course, first of all I looked for the fifty "Orphic Sayings" by A. Bronson Alcott, and I read them aloud, full of pride and appreciation to see them in print. What did it matter that *The Dial* could not afford to pay its contributors?

Some of the Sayings I found somewhat abstruse, yet provocative. I tried to keep one awesome thought from chilling my enthusiasm—the thought of what literary critics in Boston might say about such typical Alcott expressions as "Your first duty is self-culture, self-exaltation: you may not violate this high trust," or "The voice of the private, not popular heart, is alone authentic."

Best of all, I liked the thirty-fifth Saying, which I

copied off in Anna's and Louisa's diaries:

> . . . "nature is not separate from me; she is mine alike with my body; and in moments of true life I feel my identity with her; I breathe, pulsate, feel, think, will, through her members. . . ."

Of course, the girls were too young to grasp the full meaning of their father's words, but I was sure they would get glimmers of truth, and I felt that Louisa, especially as she grew older, would appreciate her father's closeness to nature.

Mr. Emerson had two poems in that first issue of *The Dial*, Margaret Fuller an essay, and Henry Thoreau some prose and poetry. It seemed almost like a family magazine.

Although Mr. Emerson thought the Orphic Sayings were "of great importance," because they set *The Dial* apart from other journals, the Boston papers were quick to criticize them. In fact, most of the critical assault on the new magazine fell on my husband's contribution. Commentators went so far as to write contemptuous parodies on the Sayings.

Although carrying on a constant duel with my temper, I found it impossible not to berate the critics. But my husband went his way without comment, working in his garden, helping me with the housework, tutoring Anna and Lu, meeting with the poor children of the village once a week to teach them, and working in our neighbors' fields for whatever they would pay him. In the evening he read, and wrote more Orphic Sayings. With perfect composure he collected the critics' parodies and pasted the worst of them into his Journal. I even saw him indexing them under P . . . "Parodies on Orphic Sayings," with his customary neatness.

I felt great compassion for him. He was so continually occupied, yet in the coin of the day he seemed to achieve so little. Surely, surely, I thought over and over again, there must be some place in the world for a gentleman-philosopher who is also willing to be a day laborer.

CHAPTER 8

NEAR THE END OF JULY, the year we moved to Concord, our fourth girl was born. I had only one name picked out for the expected baby—A. Bronson Alcott, after his father. I had been so sure it would be a boy. Now, disappointed, I turned to my husband. His gentle reply lifted the disappointment from my heart. "I have already thought of a name, my dear. The baby must be named Abba May after her mother." He pressed my hand.

In August, not long after the baby's birth, I was surprised when Mr. Alcott came to me and asked if I minded if he left me for a week. "What for?" I asked, more than a little sharply. I knew that the garden needed constant care in the middle of the growing season. Then the happy thought crossed my mind that perhaps someone from a neighboring town had offered him a week's work in the fields. "Will you be working?"

"No," he admitted. "There is a gathering of Millerites and Come-Outers at Groton, Abba. George Ripley, Theodore Parker, and Christopher Cranch are walking out from Boston today, to spend the night at the Emersons'. I would like to join them tomorrow and finish the journey with them . . . twenty-five miles over the hills to Groton."

I felt a little impatient and sorry for myself. I could picture them talking, talking, talking as they walked through the summer countryside without a care on their minds, leaving me at home with a new baby and three other children to care for. But before I could make any comment, my husband added hastily: "I have arranged for the eldest Hosmer boy to take care of the chores, and for a neighbor girl to come in to help you, Abba."

His face was so full of boyish eagerness, I held my peace. I knew what delight he took in reform meetings of this kind, partly out of curiosity, partly to listen to other ideas and offer some of his own. Personally I had little interest in the Millerites, who were predicting the second coming of Christ on October 22, 1843. But I did sympathize with the Come-Outers who refused to have anything to do with the Church because of its hypocrisy on the slavery issue. They went to extremes, of course, believing that money should be abandoned because capitalists and merchants and all rich people were in favor of slavery.

I smiled at him. "You promise to tell me all about it when you come back?" I asked.

He nodded happily.

He came back with a full account of the gatherings for me and an unusual story for the girls. Louisa listened wide-eyed when he said he had seen the most famous flowing beard in the United States.

"What's a beard for?" asked Louisa.

"That, Louisa, is what a great many other people ask. Beards don't happen to be in style these days, but Mr. Palmer wears one, anyway." Mr. Alcott paused, then went on dramatically. "He even had to spend some months in jail because of his refusal to cut off his famous beard."

"Why doesn't he want to cut it off?"

"He says if God in all his wisdom has given him a beard, he is not going to undo a work of God."

"And so he will wear it all his life," Louisa said solemnly, finishing the story.

"He even plans to have a picture of it carved on his tombstone." My husband turned to me. "I liked Joseph Palmer, Abba. And I have reason to believe that he liked me. We had a number of talks together."

"Oh, I wish you had brought him home with you, Papa, so I could see his beard," Louisa said.

The children were used to having strangers and "individualists" at our home for a day, a week, even a month. Brother Sam's parsonage was a station on the Underground Railroad, and he occasionally sent fugitives on their way via the Alcotts'. Besides, every house we lived in seemed to be a magnet for reformer friends of my husband. Sometimes I got impatient, especially when our cupboard was already bare, but mostly they were simple souls, confident that they could reform the world, and one could not help but sympathize with them.

"Why didn't you bring the bearded man home with you, Papa?" Louy persisted.

I smiled to myself. I had no doubt that sooner or later Joseph Palmer and his famous beard would appear on our doorstep.

Our routine of living in Hosmer's little brown cottage was simple. We were up early, soon after dawn, because we all wanted to crowd so many things into each day. After our breakfast, my husband tutored the girls. They practiced reading, writing and spelling, and he talked with them about the Bible and Christian's many trials in *Pilgrim's Progress*, and conscience, and obedience, and other subjects that might come up. After his school work was over, Mr. Alcott turned to the hard physical work awaiting him outdoors. In the evening he often conducted a Conversation at a home in some nearby town, or in Mr. Emerson's great white house, or in our own little parlor.

While Mr. Alcott worked in the garden or at the woodpile, I had my hands full with work indoors. I washed and ironed, baked and cooked and scrubbed. The girls helped with some of the housework, and tomboy Louisa also helped with the chores—carrying in wood, taking out ashes, feeding the chickens. I tried to make the girls enjoy work that would otherwise have been drudgery. My way was never to scold them. Whenever Louisa was upset over the way things were at home, which was often, I would give her time for second thought. Or I would write her a little note pointing out why something had gone wrong, and then she was always ready to try again. I made it a habit to write the girls almost daily letters to help them meet their trials. Their father often wrote them notes too, and whenever they were away visiting relatives, he wrote them especially helpful and affectionate letters.

For dinner I always served something substantial like squash or potatoes or rice, with a bit of cheese or meat or eggs for the girls and me, if possible. I felt the need of meat once in a while, even if the vegetarian head of the household scorned the thought of it. And I had my way about this, although Mr. Alcott did his best to convert the girls by putting little cards at their plates, poking fun at the meat-eating habit. Surprisingly enough, he seemed none the worse for clinging to his vegetarian diet.

Our evening meal was simple, usually whole-grain bread, fruit and nuts, but our table talk soared. My husband had the art of making any subject interesting, and he drew us all under his spell.

We would both tell stories often. His were imaginative and allegorical, mine true to life but not always practical in spite of it. Telling stories was my way of getting the girls to know their family background. Louisa was fascinated by the tales I remembered hearing my father tell of Revolutionary and witchcraft days. She seemed to have inherited some of his undoubted gift for narration.

The children learned a great deal from our table talk, a custom we never abandoned. And there would often be valuable discussions attuned to Louisa's special needs, such as the difference between temper and temperament, or between temperamental and mental.

After supper when the dishes had been washed and put away, and if need be the bread set, I would take my mending basket and listen to the evening reading. Our favorite book was *Pilgrim's Progress*, and hearing it through my husband's voice, I discovered new values in it that I had missed as a child. *Philothea*, written by our good friend Maria Child, was another great favorite. The Greek setting of the novel gave the girls an excellent background in history as the romantic plot unfolded. They were eager to make it into a play and they worked at it for a long time before we finally saw them act out the parts.

I had my first real letter from Louisa late that summer. Word had come from Boston that my father was ill, and so I hurried to the old house on Federal Street, taking the baby with me. Some days later a letter to "Dearest Mother" arrived, neat and unblotted. Louisa, not yet eight, was continuing the family tradition of letter writing.

My father's health improved within a few weeks, and I came home to find that Louisa had a new, magic friend—Henry Thoreau. She had formed the habit of following when he took his class on an excursion through the woods or swamps or meadows. "He knows the best places to find *everything*," she told me, her dark eyes gleaming. "Berries and lichen and animal tracks and arrowheads and birds . . . and everything. And he has a boat, and he gave us a ride on the river!"

My husband, quite as much as Louisa, was astonished by Henry Thoreau's knowledge of nature. "There is not bird nor flower or tree that man cannot name!" he exclaimed. "I have not the slightest doubt that he has many of the qualities of genius. How blessed we are in Concord to have both Mr. Emerson and Henry Thoreau."

In the meantime, Henry Thoreau's mother became my friend. I was drawn to her at once when I learned that she was a founder of the Concord Women's Anti-Slavery Society, and was active in town affairs. She had a strong personality, and was never afraid to say what she thought. And she was the kind of woman who would do without luxuries on the table so that her two daughters might have music lessons. From the first I could see how her son Henry came by his interest in nature. In the early years of their marriage,

Mrs. Thoreau and her husband had explored all the country around Concord. They knew, before Henry did, where "everything" could be found.

My husband and I were invited to Emersons' on a number of occasions when visitors were there from Boston. But sometimes I was unable to go because of the children or duties at home. One occasion I regretted missing that fall was the visit of Margaret Fuller and the Rev. George Ripley and his wife. They came to discuss with Mr. Emerson a plan that had circulated among the Transcendentalists for some time, a plan for a communal-living project. I already knew the general idea—a farm community where members could live and work together, where culture and labor, thinking and working, might be combined. It was not a new idea, of course. Years before, Robert Owen's Utopian colony on the banks of the Wabash River had tried communal living and failed. So had other similar projects. But Mr. Ripley had confidence that he could make his Brook Farm community succeed.

When my husband came home late that evening, I plied him with questions. "What does Mr. Emerson think? Would he join such a group? Is he enthusiastic?" I knew Mr. Emerson's opinion would carry weight, for he was already a national figure as a writer and lecturer.

"As a matter of fact, he said very little," my husband recalled. "He is too much of an individualist to become involved in a community project like Brook

Farm. As you and I know, he needs to be alone much of the time, thinking and writing. I suggested as much to Mr. Ripley when I commented that the farm would be no place for a writer."

"And he agreed?"

"Quite the contrary. He was quick to point out that Nathaniel Hawthorne of Salem also felt that he must be alone much of the time, to write. But Mr. Hawthorne is willing . . . not only willing, but eager . . . to buy stock in the Brook Farm venture. He expects to be able to write and at the same time to do his share of manual work."

"And what do *you* think?" I asked, looking up from my mending and blinking my eyes to rest them. The lamp wick had crept up and made a smoky smudge on the chimney, dimming the light.

"I think, my dear, that the whole project smacks too much of arithmetic."

I smiled to myself, knowing all too well my husband's aversion to arithmetic.

"Members are to be paid a dollar a day for work," he went on, "physical or mental, and they are to pay the actual cost of food, fuel, clothing, and housing for themselves and their families. Too complicated, I say, and too practical. Though Mr. Emerson says 'too *im*-practical.' " He shook his head. "I am afraid the plan will fail for lack of discipline."

"I can't help wondering who will do the 'Martha' work," I mused. "The endless washing, scrubbing, baking, cooking, mending, cleaning . . . who will do that while others talk half the night or dance over the green?"

My husband nodded. "Margaret Fuller is not convinced either. Her comment was terse and to the point. 'How much nobler stands a man entirely unpledged, unbound,' she said. I am afraid the Ripleys received little encouragement from the three of us."

November came and with it our first taste of cold weather. But since most of the harvest was gathered in, I felt reassured. Carrots, turnips, onions, potatoes, and cabbage were stored in the earth-cellar under the kitchen, along with barrels of apples given us by neighbors for helping them pick their crop. Squash, parsley, and mint I had dried. Corn, beans, and peas, shucked and shelled, were safe in the barn in mouse-tight boxes. And my husband had a good start on the woodpile we would need to carry us over the winter. Whatever else happened, we would not go hungry or cold for many months.

Of course, we still had to buy some things in the village—flour, sugar, tea (my weakness), salt, cheese, and, all too rarely, meat.

On the 29th of November we celebrated the first dual birthday in the little cottage, Louisa's eighth birthday and her father's forty-first. And a happy Sunday birthday it turned out to be. Outdoors all morning a bright cold wind tore at the brooding sky and piled leaves along the hedgerows. Indoors we basked in warmth and cheer. Weeks before, Louisa had told me that she and Anna and Elizabeth wanted to act out parts of *Pilgrim's Progress* for their father's birthday. We worked hard at it—sewing costumes, rehearsing lines. Both Anna and Louisa showed considerable dramatic ability, I thought, losing themselves in their roles. Their father was delighted with his unusual present. For his part, he prepared an artistic birthday letter for Louisa, illustrated with pictures that he drew.

By afternoon the cold wind died down, and the children were able to play outdoors with their friends until dusk. Then I invited them all into the parlor for a "party." I had little to make a party of. But by cutting the bread into thin square pieces, I made it look different. And by slicing apples and arranging the slices decoratively on a plate, I made them look different, too. Louisa, I am sure, felt no lack; the spirit of a happy birthday filled the room.

My husband came and stood in the doorway, watching. I smiled at him, though at the same time a pang of realization made me catch my breath. He still stood slender and tall—nearly six feet—and he was still handsome, with serene blue eyes, blond hair, and that strange but attractive pucker in his chin. But I saw deepened furrows on his face, and thinning and fading in his hair that fell in long strands behind his ears. I even saw some hairs of white! Suddenly I knew that he looked older than his years, older than he should look at forty-one. The failure of Temple School had taken its toll.

CHAPTER 9

NO MATTER HOW CONSCIENTIOUSLY I economized or how hard my husband worked, we rarely were able to meet our monthly expenses, even when the garden was producing abundantly. In good weather Mr. Alcott went about conducting Conversations at Hingham, Scituate, Marshfield, Providence, and other towns, and even at Mr. Ripley's new community of Brook Farm, eight miles from Boston. As his fee my husband took whatever his listeners cared to give him, and he never complained when he had little to bring home for his time and trouble. Times were especially hard for us as cold weather closed in. Traveling became difficult, and little work was available in the neighborhood. A dollar a day for chopping wood, when wood needed to be chopped, seemed to be the best Mr. Alcott could do. Needless to say, we were in debt to some of the merchants in Concord.

I was hopeful that a way would open up for me to get my husband some writing paper for Christmas. I knew he had been out of paper for his Journal for some time. Paper was expensive, especially the good quality he liked for his Journal. For weeks he had been writing his daily record on any old scrap he could lay his hands on, carefully tying the scraps together in order, biding his time patiently until he could get good paper to copy them on.

One night when Mr. Emerson dropped in for a visit, a question came up about the date of a certain lecture a month or two before. My husband went to get his scraps, thumbed through them quickly, and found the date. "These are all to be copied in my Journal in due time," he explained to Mr. Emerson apologetically.

Later when Mr. Alcott left the room to find a book, I saw Mr. Emerson busy himself over the table for a moment, picking up the copy of Coleridge my husband was currently rereading. After our guest left I opened the book. There lay a ten dollar bill. It was not the first time our good neighbor had left a bill to meet some need he discovered. With a welling up of gratitude, I left the surprise in the book and slipped off to the kitchen.

At times I felt discouraged, almost despondent, by the outlook, and I am sure Mr. Alcott did, too, in spite of his abounding faith that the good Lord would take care of us. His religion was never a one-day-in-seven matter, but something he tried to live day in and day out. He gave more than lip-service to his belief that God dwells in each and every one of us. And he lived up to his belief by being unfailingly kind under provocations that made me lose my temper and say sharp words that I regretted later.

Things had been going badly, too, for our friends the Childs on their sugar-beet farm. Their experiments suffered from lack of money, equipment, and labor. David was sure that it was practical to make beet sugar in the United States, but he could not do it single-handed. He won an award of one hundred dollars for his sugar at one Massachusetts exhibition, and a silver medal at another, yet no one seemed willing to invest money to carry on the experiments on a large enough scale to make them profitable.

"He's too far ahead of his time," my husband said when I read him Maria's letter about their troubles.

Maria went on to say that she was leaving soon for New York to become editor of the *National Anti-Slavery Standard*. It took all her courage to be away from David, who felt he could not give up his experiments. "I would not go," she said, "except that we need the money so desperately. I am ready to do anything to pay off our debts."

I felt the same way. But I did not know what I could do, or where I could turn.

Our affairs were at a very low ebb that winter when my dear cousin Hannah Robie came from Boston to visit us. It was she who had given me the lovely silver dish for a wedding present. She brought along a big bundle of clothes for the girls from a friend whose children had been pupils at Temple School. My husband sat serenely by, watching the girls and Miss Robie and me sort out the clothes to see what could be made over.

"These are for *me*," Louisa cried, pouncing on a pair of leather boots with high soft tops. "Anna can have the dresses."

We all laughed when Louisa tried on the boots, sizes too big for her, and paraded around like a prince of the Indies.

"I told you not to be anxious about clothes for the girls," Mr. Alcott said. "Here we have not only clothes but a striking pair of boots for Prince Louy."

It was often that way, I had to admit. I did the worrying and he did the trusting, and more often than not things came out his way.

Another time it was wood I was worrying about. The weather had turned cold and a storm threatened, and our supply of wood was low. My husband had been too busy chopping for others to replenish our pile. Still he gave half of it away to a needy family in the neighborhood when he discovered that their supply was about gone and their baby was sick.

I began to object. "But our little Abba May will suffer from cold . . ."

"Either the weather will moderate," my husband replied confidently, "or the Lord will provide us with wood."

Snow began to fall and the storm grew worse by the hour as the afternoon wore on. Windblown snow swirled around the cottage and sifted in under the door until I 'stuffed the cracks with old stockings. Then suddenly Louisa, standing at the window, sang out, quoting from a favorite poem Maria Child had written:

> *"The horse knows the way*
> *To carry the sleigh*
> *Through the white and drifted snow."*

A farmer turned in at the gate with a load of wood he was taking to town, and asked if he could leave it with us before the storm got worse. "No need to pay for it till you're good and ready," he assured us. "I'm just hankering to unload it and get home as fast as I can."

Again my husband's trust had been rewarded and my worry rebuked.

During my cousin's visit, the two of us went to call on a needy family. I was surprised when the woman mentioned that my husband had already been there. She said that he had come on two different days to chop wood for her. How like him, I thought, not to let me know! He had such a quiet way of being where he was needed, and, after taking care of the need, slipping quietly away again.

Whenever our debts worried me unduly, I found special comfort in knowing that Mr. Emerson never sat in judgment on my husband for not making more effort to pay them. Mr. Emerson felt that a man had a right to ask himself which debt he must pay first—the debt of money, or the debt of thought to mankind. To a man like Bronson Alcott money was of small importance, but sharing love, faith, and aspiration was sacred. In the payment of these debts he never failed.

Our friendship with the Emersons deepened with every month that passed, and I often thought that, had there been no other reason for moving to Concord, living near them would have been more than enough. My husband and Mr. Emerson seemed to supplement each other. Both were stimulated to great heights by their discussions. I enjoyed Mrs. Emerson's company, and the girls liked nothing better than to "run over to Emersons'" to play with Waldo and little Ellen.

That first winter we were at the Cottage, Mr. Emerson made a proposition that surprised both my husband and me. We knew that he was too much of an individualist to be attracted by the idea of a community like Brook Farm. Yet he was stirred by the need for social reform and wanted to keep an open mind.

Finally he decided to experiment on a limited scale himself.

One gray winter afternoon when we walked over for a Sunday call, he asked suddenly, "What would you Alcotts think of moving in with us for a year? What would you think of joining us in a program combining labor and plain living? We have been thinking it over, Lidian and I, and the idea appeals to us both."

My first reaction was favorable. For the first time in years we would have security. Although Mr. Emerson was by no means a wealthy man, he had an income separate from his earnings as a lecturer and writer. For an entire year we would not have to worry about having a roof over our heads or abundant food on the table. My husband and Mr. Emerson would enjoy their intellectual companionship as well as their physical work together. I admired Lidian Emerson and saw no reason why we could not get along in the same household. The proposition was tempting indeed.

Mr. Alcott and I talked it over from all angles. In the end we decided that, poor as we were, our independence was too precious to lose. We would manage somehow at the Cottage.

In the meantime the Thoreau brothers had closed their school because of John's ill health. And so Mr. Emerson tried out his plan of cooperation by asking Henry Thoreau to come for a year to do whatever labor he chose for a few hours a day in return for board and room.

This plan of limited cooperation worked out very well. Lidian Emerson had as warm a motherly interest in young Henry Thoreau as I had myself. He was twenty-three years old, self-sufficient, quiet, and talented in many ways. He always found plenty of work to do in the garden and house, but he was never too busy to ride Ellen on his shoulders or to make a whistle or a boat for Waldo. As for Mr. Emerson, he was so delighted with the experiment in cooperative living that he asked Henry to come for a second year.

Before the winter was over, I was called to Boston by the death of my father. He had been in ill health for some months, but I had fully expected him to recover. To me he had always been the embodiment of stamina and strength that could not be shaken. The realization that I would never visit with him again or listen to his stories was a severe blow. Now Brother Sam and I were the only two left of a large family.

In his Will, my father left me $3100, but with strings attached. I suppose he knew that if I received the sum outright, it would be taken over immediately by our creditors. And so he provided that the money should be invested, with Brother Sam and Cousin Samuel Sewall supervising the account. This, I knew, was best. I was grateful for my father's foresight and for the yearly interest I would receive.

In April we celebrated our first anniversary at Hosmer Cottage. It had been a happy family year in spite of our money problems. And now that we had survived the winter and robins were singing once more, the future looked brighter. Soon Mr. Alcott would be out working the earth and planting his garden.

One day when the last of the snowbanks were melting, Louisa came running to me with a heart-warming surprise. She had been breathing deeply of spring, listening to the robins, and putting her thoughts on paper. I never will forget how she came, full of excitement, her dark eyes aglow. "Marmee! I thought of a song. I wrote it over three times . . . so Papa couldn't say it wasn't neat." She handed me a paper full of the uncertain writing of an 8-year-old. I read the words aloud:

TO THE FIRST ROBIN

Welcome, welcome, little stranger,
Fear no harm, and fear no danger;
We are glad to see you here,
For you sing, "Sweet Spring is near."

Now the white snow melts away;
Now the flowers blossom gay;
Come dear bird and build your nest,
For we love our robin best.

It seemed almost too good to be true. "Oh, Louy," I exclaimed, "You may grow up to be a poet! You must write down all your songs."

Like both their parents, Anna and Louisa wrote in

their journals regularly. They knew we inspected them to check on their spelling and penmanship, but that did not seem to keep them from recording their innermost thoughts and feelings. Writing came easily to them both, a fact that I ascribed to practice as much as anything else.

Our second summer at the Cottage passed quickly. Before we knew it, the garden was harvested, the apples picked, and Mr. Alcott was confidently sharpening his axe, hoping to chop mountains of wood for his well-earned dollar a day. But before he started off to solicit his first order one autumn morning, Louisa came dashing into the kitchen. "The beard!" she cried. "It's coming down the road. Two of them! Come, see, Papa."

We hurried to the front room window. There sure enough were two patriarchs of old walking down the road, turning in at our gate. One beard was more majestic than the other.

"Joseph Palmer himself!" my husband exclaimed. "And that must be his friend Abraham Everett. Two of our leading Come-Outers."

"Bearded individualists," I sighed. "You didn't tell me there were two in the movement. I suppose they go around together to protect their beards."

If my husband heard my remark, he paid no attention. He was already hurrying out to welcome the men, with Louisa beside him, fascinated.

In a way I was fascinated, too. I admired Joseph

Palmer for holding to his principles in spite of scorn and jail sentences. Just the day before I had heard my husband tell Anna: "Say Yes or No, Anna, not to please others but your own conscience." I could well understand why he gave the bearded men a hearty welcome.

The two men stayed a week with us in our crowded quarters, talking, talking—planning utopias and solving the problems of the world. Both, I thought, showed uncommon good sense in some of their remarks about farming and communal living. They were kind to the children and often gave me a helping hand with the work. On the last day of the visit, they organized a wood-chopping party that did wonders for the Alcott woodpile. I was not at all surprised, after our visitors left, to have Louisa come to me and ask earnestly, "Why *shouldn't* a man wear a beard if he wants to? I *like* beards."

A week before Louisa's ninth birthday, Mr. Emerson walked over in the late afternoon with the news of the birth of a second daughter. "I think Waldo would like to name her Louy," he said, putting his arm around Louy's shoulder, "but my wife and I have already decided on Edith."

"Edith and Ellen sound very well together, for sisters," I remarked. "How fortunate you were, Mr. Emerson, that your first child was a son."

"Yes, Mrs. Alcott, I am fortunate indeed to have Waldo. I don't know what I would do without him."

CHAPTER 10

JANUARY 1842 WAS A MONTH we Alcotts and other folk of Concord would gladly have omitted from our lives. Two tragedies struck in quick succession, bringing grief to two leading families and making us all realize the transitoriness of life.

On New Year's Day Henry Thoreau's brother John cut the end of one of his fingers. He put on a bandage and thought nothing of it. Several days later the finger suddenly began to hurt, the pain quickly spread, and lockjaw set in. The Thoreaus called in a doctor from Boston, but it was too late. Nothing could be done. With superhuman courage John endured the agony of his pain comforted by his brother Henry's almost continual nursing. On the afternoon of January 11, John died in Henry's arms.

Our hearts went out to Henry even more than to

the grieving parents. We knew how attached to each other the two brothers had been, and we knew something of the depth of Henry's feelings. At first he seemed calm enough. But soon his calm turned to morbid silence. Mr. Alcott came home from a call at the Thoreau home to say that all the time he was there Henry had said not one single word.

Then in a few days we heard that Henry had become seriously ill himself, showing all the symptoms of lockjaw. "He has brought it upon himself by his brooding," my husband said, aghast. "I must try to comfort him."

No one ever knew what happened to shake Henry from the grip of his illness, but several days later he began to get better. Slowly, slowly he recovered.

On the 24th of January, just two days after Henry's turn for the better, we heard the distressing news that 5-year-old Waldo Emerson was down with scarlatina. I knew this to be a mild form of scarlet fever, and so was confident there was nothing to worry about. How dear the boy was to us all!

We heard no news for several days. The weather was blustery and cold, and so I kept the children indoors most of the time. But finally the sun came out and the wind died down. Louisa, bursting with pent-up energy, asked if she might run down the road to inquire about Waldo. She and Waldo were great friends, even though Louisa was four years older.

When Louy came home, I knew at once that something was wrong. She ran to me and buried her head in my apron. "I saw Mr. Emerson's face," she sobbed. "He looked so sad, Marmee. Waldo . . . Waldo's dead."

I held her tightly. For several minutes she could not control her sobs. Then she turned her tear-streaked face to mine. "Now there won't be anyone to tell Mr. Emerson not to dig his leg."

"That beautiful boy!" Mr. Alcott exclaimed when we told him the sad news. "Oh, my poor friend. What can I say to him? And to Henry Thoreau who loved him, too. That beautiful boy!"

"Henry and Mr. Emerson are both Transcendentalists," I said hopefully. "Surely something in their belief will help them, even as little Josiah Quincy's words helped me."

"The human mind finds it hard to philosophize at a time like this," came the quiet reply. "But the spiritual ultimately transcends the material . . . if not today, then tomorrow."

It was so with Mr. Emerson. At first his grief almost overwhelmed him. At the funeral it seemed to me that neither he nor his wife could ever be the same again, so bowed down were they by their sorrow. But gradually they accepted their loss and built a new life without their boy. In time Mr. Emerson was even able to write an ode in honor of his son and nature:

> "The hyacinthine boy, for whom
> Morn well might break and April bloom . . ."

Two weeks after the burial of little Waldo, Mr. Emerson had to leave for Providence to fill a lecture engagement. Much to our surprise he took time to write us a letter. He had been concerned over our money worries for a long time, and had come to the conclusion that something could be done to give my husband a new start. And so he wrote that it would probably not cost more than four or five hundred dollars for Mr. Alcott to spend the summer in England with his friends at Alcott House.

"But where will the money come from?" I blurted out, as I listened to Mr. Alcott read the letter.

Mr. Emerson had foreseen the question, and he had the answer ready. It would give him great pleasure, he wrote, to pay the sum and more if need be.

My husband's face lighted up and the lines of discouragement suddenly vanished. "A summer in England!" he breathed. "I can think of no place in the world I would rather go."

We began at once to make plans for the journey. It seemed to us that this might well be the turning point in his life. With hope in my heart I set about getting my husband's well-worn clothes in order. I cleaned and mended, sponged and pressed, and did what I could to make him presentable to his English friends.

I was in the midst of packing Mr. Alcott's trunk, the first week in May, when Margaret Fuller decided to come to Concord to visit the Emersons. Mr. Emerson brought her to call on us one afternoon. Having worked with my husband at Temple School, she knew about his educational methods and his desire to bring up his girls as "model children."

The afternoon of the call I had whisked my mending basket and ironing board out of sight and prevailed upon the girls to play outdoors so we could enjoy our talk. All went well until our guests were about to leave, in fact, until they were at the door. Then Margaret, giving a quick glance around, remarked: "Well, Mr. Alcott, have you been able to carry out your ideas with your family? By the way, where *are* your model children?"

At that point I heard a great uproar coming around the corner of the house. First Louisa appeared, acting like a horse, with a bit and bridle and rope reins. Beside her little Lizzie, a "dog," barked and jumped. Then in a cart guided by Anna and pulled by the "horse" sat Abba May, not yet two years old, dressed in a curtain like a queen. They were having an uproarious time until, all of a sudden, they saw us at the door. Louisa stopped so quickly she tripped on the cart, and they all went down in a heap, laughing.

"There," I said to Miss Fuller with a dramatic gesture, "there are the model children."

Mr. Alcott made arrangements with his young brother Junius to stay with us over the summer. Junius, my husband's favorite brother, was only about ten years older than Anna. I was pleased to have him come, and Junius himself seemed glad for the change.

His four nieces were devoted admirers from the beginning.

All too soon the day came for my husband to take the stage to Boston, to catch the ship sailing from Boston harbor. Junius borrowed a horse and wagon from Mr. Hosmer and drove his brother to the stage. It was all I could do to hold back the tears while the girls and I waved from the gate until the wagon was out of sight. Then I hurried to my room, buried my face in my hands, and had a good cry. I wanted my husband to go; I wanted him to see Alcott House and talk with the men whose praise would mean so much to him. Yet I couldn't help feeling sorry for myself. I dreaded the loneliness and the responsibility of caring for the children without him.

I knew it would be many weeks before I could hope to hear from him. The journey alone would take three weeks, and it would take another three weeks before his first letter could reach me. Alone on the 23rd of May, my twelfth wedding anniversary, I wrote in my journal that my years with Bronson Alcott had been great years for my soul. I tried to be patient in my loneliness.

Junius helped fill the gap. He was thoughtful around the house, a good gardener, an ingenious "fixer," and he cheered us all with his fun-loving ways. He and I planned picnics and celebrations to liven the weeks for the girls. But in spite of everything they missed their father, and every day they wreathed his picture with wildflowers. The feeling of loneliness grew on me. My husband was the kindest, wisest man I knew. It was like trying to do without breath, I wrote in my journal, to get along without him.

Finally the yearned-for first letter arrived, giving us news of the journey. I smiled at Mr. Alcott's mention of the cottage bread, the apples, and the applesauce he had taken with him from home, and of how sustaining they had been when supplemented by the ship's potatoes. With a grateful heart I learned that he had stood the journey well.

A second letter a few days later told how he had taken lodgings in London and walked to see St. Paul's Cathedral. He was disappointed in it. He found it overlaid with too much ornament for his taste. He could not, he wrote, imagine any spiritual inspiration in such an ornate edifice . . . only dogma and ritual and empty echoes of holy things. After his first days in London he came to the conclusion that everything around him was solid and substantial, but all for the body and not for the spirit.

Even Westminster Abbey disappointed my idealistic husband. He entered during the chanting of prayers and responses from the choir, and felt that the service, though of historical interest, was merely a spectacle, "a masked, ignoble show." And the Gothic Abbey itself impressed him as no more than a monument to man's fallen greatness.

On his arrival at Alcott House in Surrey, not far

from London, he was deeply shocked and grieved to learn that the man he had been corresponding with for years, the one man in England he wanted most to meet, had died some weeks before. Through their extensive correspondence, my husband knew that he and Mr. Greaves had a great deal in common. No one in England could take his place in my husband's esteem and affection, although he received a most cordial welcome from Mr. Lane and Mr. Wright who were running Alcott House.

I saved all my husband's letters, of course, and read them over and over. Nearly every morning at the breakfast table, I read aloud the letter he had written to the girls, feeling that it would set their feet along the proper path for the day:

"My dear Girls:

I think of you all every day and desire to see you all again: Anna with her beauty-loving eyes and sweet visions of graceful motions—Louisa with her quick and ready services, her agile limbs and boundless curiosity, her penetrating mind and tear-shedding heart, alive to all moving, breathing things—Elizabeth with her quiet-loving disposition and serene thoughts, her happy gentleness, deep sentiment—and last, but yet dearest too in her joys and impetuous griefs, the little Abba with her fast falling footsteps, her sagacious eye and auburn locks . . ."

Mr. Alcott had been gone just two months when Nathaniel Hawthorne brought his bride to live in Concord at the old Manse. His bride was none other than Sophia Peabody, Elizabeth Peabody's younger sister who had taken her place for a while at Temple School.

Mr. Hawthorne was already quite well-known as the author of *Twice-Told Tales* and other stories and the Peabody sisters—Elizabeth, Sophia, and Mary—had a prominence of their own in Boston and Salem. And so there was a flurry of excitement in our village over the opening of the old Manse which had been rented by the bride and groom.

The rest of July passed somehow, with part of me in England with my husband and part of me in Concord enjoying the children and Junius. As little Abba's second birthday approached, Louisa bubbled over with excitement, for her Uncle Junius had promised a special celebration for that day. I packed a picnic basket and we walked to the river in high spirits, with Uncle Junius pulling the basket and baby in the four-wheeled cart. I had no inkling that the special secret would turn out to be a boating excursion to the Cliffs up the river.

Junius rowed us there in his boat, the "Water Spirit." After our picnic lunch we played games, and the girls raced with their uncle, but not until they had partly tied his feet as a handicap. All the while, part of me kept thinking about my husband, for I knew full well that he would remember the birthday even though he was so far away. Birthday celebrations were our way of expressing the joy we felt in the birth of our children and in being able to have them with us as we made our way along the path of life.

CHAPTER 11

MEANWHILE ACROSS THE SEA my husband had not been forming a very flattering opinion of the English people, except for the reformers he met through Alcott House. He was already well acquainted with the work of two noted men he met—George Thompson, the lecturer against slavery, who had been mobbed in Boston in 1835; and Robert Owen, founder of the New Harmony colony in Indiana. But for the most part, the meat-eating habits of Englishmen distressed him, and he felt that the men lorded it over their women folk.

The biggest disappointment of all turned out to be the man he had looked up to for years as the greatest leader of reform in England—Thomas Carlyle. He was a friend of Mr. Emerson's and had been almost an idol of my husband's. Mr. Emerson sent Mr. Carlyle a letter to alert him to my husband's coming, and we fully expected that one of the high points of the journey would be their meeting.

But somehow from the first they did not take to each other. Even Mr. Carlyle's appearance was a shock. Apparently my husband expected him to be an ascetic, slender man with an animated face and unforgettable eyes. But what he saw was a heavily-built body, tired eyes, and a deeply furrowed face framed by a mass of tousled iron-gray hair. He expected Mr. Carlyle to be courteous and gentlemanly like Mr. Emerson, and instead he found him to be crotchety and ill-mannered, a great talker, impatient of any interruption. Far from leading any movement for reform in England, he was thoroughly disgusted with the England of his day. He insisted that the past, bad as it was, was better than the present, and so he had been digging out dull, dusty records of the past, and writing a book on Oliver Cromwell. But he reviled the task for wearing him out. His conversation was cynical and turbulent and it gave my husband no pleasure. Even at mealtime there was no serenity. After a second disappointing visit, my husband tried once more, and that time the two men quarreled outright. He never attempted to see Mr. Carlyle again.

Of course, I never breathed a word of all this to the Emersons, for Mr. Emerson liked England and the English, and was not Bronson Alcott seeing the country on Emerson money? I decided that my poor husband probably missed his "cottage bread," which he liked to make himself of unbolted flour and water, and he probably couldn't find any good apples in London markets.

Fortunately his stay at Alcott House turned out to be all that he hoped for. He wrote me detailed letters about it. There in a large and attractive building he found a school run on a combination of his principles and Pestalozzi's. The two books the teachers relied on most were Miss Peabody's *Record of a School* and his own *Conversations with Children* which had been so berated in Boston. Though rejected in his home country, at Alcott House he was looked upon as an outstanding authority.

Mr. Emerson gloried with me in the news. This was a taste of the pure success we both felt Mr. Alcott needed. We were delighted to hear about the leading Transcendentalists and reformers he was meeting at Alcott House, writers and editors and thinkers, all of whom looked up to Mr. Alcott with admiration and respect. During the four months of his visit he was kept very busy delivering lectures on education, writing articles, and studying the work done at Alcott House.

At home the girls became immersed in theatrical projects, which made the time go fast and pleasantly for all of us. They turned the barn into a playhouse, using old sheets on a rope for a curtain, and relying on

Uncle Junius to provide plank seats for the audience. Anna and Louisa spent hours dramatizing stories they knew, and making up little plays of their own. They spent days rehearsing and sewing costumes. Sometimes the two older girls took several parts each, and became adept at making sleight-of-hand changes of costume. Louisa's boots came in handy whenever she played the part of a cavalier, or pirate, or even a pilgrim.

I helped with the costumes, and often held the prompt-book in the wings, and was as excited as the girls over the enthusiastic response of the audience. This was the beginning of an ever-growing interest in the theater on the part of both Anna and Louisa.

Toward the end of the summer disquieting news came from Alcott House. At first there was only an occasional mention of a plan for communal living in my husband's letters. But soon it became evident that Mr. Lane and Mr. Wright and my husband were seriously planning to start a "new Eden" where men might dwell in harmony. And the place for the venture was to be somewhere in New England!

Next came the news that my husband was bringing the two Englishmen and Mr. Lane's young son home with him, and they were to stay with us until they could find a suitable site for the New Eden. I was aghast at the prospect. How could we possibly manage to house them in our small cottage, especially with cold weather approaching when all five children would be underfoot? In addition, my husband spoke of boxes and boxes of books they would be bringing along, all of Mr. Greaves' private library and hundreds of other books Mr. Alcott was buying with money given him by admirers.

My husband did not seem to realize the magnitude of the housing problem. But by this time I was so eager to have him home again that I dismissed my doubts and prayed that the travelers would all arrive safely. I even went about the countryside trying to find a site for the New Eden.

Finally, toward the end of October, the homecoming day arrived. I was so joyful to see my husband that I welcomed his friends, too, with enthusiasm. After all, I had heard nothing but praise about them, which could not help but prejudice me in their favor. And for the first week I felt that we were truly blessed in having them with us, in spite of our cramped quarters.

But this joyful state did not last. All too soon our guests showed that Louisa's effervescent feelings, and mine, too, were distasteful to them. Worse still, Mr. Wright began to complain about our simple food, and he showed a marked dislike for doing any useful work about the place.

But what talk went on in our little house! My husband was in his element discussing all aspects of the "good life" with his friends. They talked about many things, particularly the slavery question, and often met with friends at Mr. Emerson's for long sessions. Little work was done to bring in money for household expenses. This was a great trial and worry to me, for the responsibility of providing three meals a day was on my shoulders. Fortunately Mr. Lane had some money.

I began to wonder how we could all continue to live amicably in our crowded cottage. Apparently Mr. Wright was having the same nagging doubts. At any rate, to my great relief, he left in about two months to live in Boston.

Now my besetting problem was how to keep up my usual high spirits in the presence of Mr. Lane whose thin lips and stubborn jaw boded ill for any sort of spontaneous living. At least Mr. Lane's young son William was not like his father, and I had no trouble in becoming fond of him. The boy was about Anna's age, quiet, refined and well-behaved, and helpful around the house. There was, I am glad to say, a re-deeming side to his father, too, for he was interested in tutoring the children. He was an educated man, musically inclined, and in addition to teaching singing to the accompaniment of his violin, he taught the children French, Latin, geography, geometry, and drawing.

As time went on Mr. Lane became more and more domineering. I had the unpleasant feeling that he had a hypnotic effect on my husband. Our simple diet was not austere enough to suit the Englishman. We had to give up molasses, milk, butter. Our family was not used to such extreme Spartan discipline as Mr. Lane advocated. If the New Eden was to be like our new life in Hosmer Cottage, I did not relish the thought of it.

I really became almost ill, thinking about it. Yet my husband listened attentively to every word Mr. Lane uttered without raising objections. I became more apprehensive with every day that passed.

It seemed to me that Mr. Emerson, too, was not at all convinced that the New Eden would work, though my husband did his best to describe the whole project on paper—the plan of the farm, the buildings, the orchard, and beautiful grounds. But how it was all to be paid for he never made clear. It was evident that Mr. Emerson found Mr. Lane a man of ability, a skillful talker, witty and resourceful, yet there was another side that Mr. Emerson had seen also. Mr. Lane was too provocative, too warlike in his manner of railing against whatever he disapproved of. I wondered if he was not wearing out his welcome at the big white house, and I was not at all surprised to find Mr. Emerson absenting himself from home for long stretches during that winter.

November 29th arrived, the day for the exchange of little gifts on Mr. Alcott's and Louisa's birthday. But the day was not a happy one for me. I felt rebuked by Mr. Lane's stiffness, almost suffocated by his restrictions. But I did manage to buy a little gift for Louisa and write her an encouraging note ending with:

> "I give you the pencil case I promised, for I have observed that you are fond of writing, and wish to encourage the habit."

Louisa was delighted. Had I given her a string of gold pieces, she could not have been more excited than she was over that pencil case.

As Christmas approached relations between me and Mr. Lane became even more strained. I feared that this foretaste of New Eden might drive me out of my mind. I no longer felt free to run my own household. My husband did not understand how much I suffered from Mr. Lane's invasion of my rights as a woman and a mother. Yet he sensed that I needed a rest, a change from our cramped quarters and endless household tasks. And so, hard as it was to leave the children, I went off to Boston for the Christmas season.

The change gave me the perspective I so sorely needed. I left home toil-worn and depressed; I came back early in January quickened by a new spirit of love and confidence. Less tenacious of my rights and opinions, I was sincerely desirous of giving the New Eden a chance. My change of attitude made all the difference. Even the cold baths both my husband and Mr. Lane advocated for winter as well as summer no longer daunted me. Sometimes water froze an inch thick in our cottage, and after it had been broken it sometimes froze again around the edges of the basin before the bath was over.

Louisa's inventiveness in making up games and telling stories saved the day more than once during inclement weather when the four Alcott girls and Willy Lane were confined to the house. And then, as an added diversion, and as a repository for the exchange of thoughts and feelings and pent-up emotions, I hit upon the idea of a household post office. At once it became popular, not only with the children, but with all of us.

I hung a basket in the entry to hold the notes and tokens to be distributed every evening after supper. If quarrels marred the day, a note of apology in the basket was a pleasant way of healing hurt feelings. Notes of approbation and kindness helped oil the wheels of family living. Each child took turns being postmaster, and with what eagerness the honor was carried out!

Plans for the New Eden continued to be discussed. Spurred on by Mr. Lane's strict ideas of diet, my husband learned to prepare our simple meals and to simplify them still further. Mr. Lane gave us all lessons in music, and taught the children to dance in the evenings. And so our days passed agreeably enough while dreams of the project in community living were taking shape.

In May Mr. Lane bought the Wyman farm near the village of Harvard, about fourteen miles from Concord, for $1800. It was not nearly as appealing to me as a farm in Lincoln that I had looked at while Mr. Alcott was still in England. But I held my peace. My husband did not like the Wyman farm either. Mr. Lane acted against his advice. I was sincerely sorry about this, for I knew that my husband's experience with New England farming made him a better judge of the land than a stranger from England.

Although I knew that there would be hardships aplenty, I hoped for the best. That there would be criticism of the venture, I was certain. Still, I entertained hope that the experiment would prove that a diverse group of people might all live the true life, putting away the evil customs of society. In spite of the uncertainties ahead, I was willing to try.

CHAPTER 12

LITTLE AS I KNEW ABOUT FARMING, I had had enough experience with our gardens in Concord to know that we were getting a late start for "the promised land." One thing after another postponed our moving date. My husband and Mr. Lane felt they had to make numerous trips to find recruits. And then at the last minute we discovered that we could not leave Concord until our local debts were paid. Mr. Lane had to dig into his pocket for another three hundred dollars. Whatever reservations I had about the man, I had to admit that he was unselfishness itself in money matters, even when he neared the end of his resources.

June was upon us before we finally said goodbye to the cottage in Concord. Surreptitiously I wiped a tear from my eye. In spite of hard times, we had spent three happy years in the little house. Abba May had been born there. We had made friends in the village. Our blue-eyed Elizabeth, not as robust as her two older sisters, had gained strength. Resolutely I shook off my depression. After all, moving was second nature to the Alcotts. We could not be sentimental about it. A new adventure lay ahead at Fruitlands.

Fruitlands was the name Mr. Lane had chosen for the place—but not because the farm boasted a thriving orchard. Only ten gnarled old apple trees, badly in need of pruning, grew on the slope. My husband assured me, though, that we would soon have an orchard planted worthy of the name. He and Mr. Lane had great plans. They spoke of little cottages in the nearest copse; of fountains at the springs above, with water descending to every cottage; of landscaped grounds and thriving gardens.

On the first of June of 1843 we were packed and ready to move. The night before, Mr. Lane had pronounced a final ultimatum: "We go whatever the weather."

The weather offered anything but a favorable portent of things to come. A cold drizzle dripped from a forbidding sky. I had an impulse to laugh as I settled myself on the wagon seat, holding the umbrella with one hand and little Abba on my lap with the other. Louisa, running up with a last package, caught my eye as she scrambled over the wagon wheel, and we exchanged silent merriment. But Mr. Alcott on the seat beside me, with the reins in his hands and Elizabeth on his knee, looked so solemn and abstracted that I stifled my mirth.

Willy Lane, holding the bust of Socrates in his arms, sat in the wagon box surrounded by household goods, looking appealingly ludicrous. Louisa settled down beside him, and pulled the end of an old blanket over their heads to keep out the drizzle. Anna and Mr. Lane walked ahead. There was no room for them in the wagon, and though I wondered if the walk might not be too much for 12-year-old Anna, I was glad Mr. Lane would be keeping his distance from me.

It was late afternoon before we left the main road and drove up the gently sloping hill to the old red farmhouse that was to be our home. We found three men already there, and the first load of furniture. One of the recruits Louisa recognized immediately as we drew up at the front door. "The lesser beard," she whispered in my ear. "Will the most famous beard be here, too?"

"Not yet, but probably soon," I replied. "Now, jump down, Louy, and ask Mr. Everett please to take the bust from Willy so it won't get broken."

By the time we unpacked dishes and pots and pans, and made supper and ate it before the open fire, the hour was late, too late to put up beds. To the delight of the girls, we all had to sleep on the floor.

The old farmhouse cried out for attention and repairs. Floors slanted at strange angles and shook underfoot when we walked. The rooms all had low ceilings, and the girls had to climb dark steep stairs to their quarters in the garret. The kitchen particularly impressed me as a drab, unhandy place to work in, day in and day out. I was making a mental list of a dozen necessary improvements when I heard my husband say, "The first and most important piece of carpentry, of course, is a hundred feet of shelves in the entry hall for the books."

Fortunately windows in the old house overlooked the gleaming Nashua River and gave us panoramas of beauty in every direction. Fields, woods, and distant mountains lay around us. Of Fruitlands' ninety acres, fourteen were wooded, affording a haven of loveliness close at hand as well.

The first chance I had to get away from the house, a few days later, the children and I walked over our hillside domain, exclaiming at the beauty of it and the variety. Often we stopped to sweep our eyes around the expanse of woodland, meadow, valley, and hills. "One is transported from his littleness," I thought to myself, "by a sight like this." While the children picked flowers, I gathered an apron of chips, and felt at peace with the world.

From the first Abraham Everett more than anyone else saw my plight as housekeeper. Along with his work in the fields, he did all he could to help me with heavy washings, incessant bread-making, and keeping the fires going. At times when our constantly changing group numbered as many as sixteen, I could not have managed without him. Silently and seriously he worked beside me, thinking profound thoughts, I was sure.

Before we had been living at Fruitlands a month, we celebrated Elizabeth's eighth birthday, making a special event of it as usual. Early in the morning, about five o'clock, Anna, Louisa, and Willy went with me to the grove to prepare a birthday setting for her. While Anna busied herself making wreaths of oak leaves for everyone, the rest of us selected a little pine tree and hung our presents on it.

After breakfast the whole Fruitlands family, wearing their oak wreaths, walked in procession to the grove. First we sang to the accompaniment of a tune Mr. Lane played on his violin. Then my husband read a parable, and after that a birthday-present ode he had written. We each chose a flower to give to Lizzie, and then she took her presents from the tree, one by one—a fan from Anna, a pincushion from Louisa, a book from Willy Lane, a little pitcher from baby Abba May, and a silk thread balloon from me. Mr. Lane's present was a poem he had written, entitled, "To Elizabeth."

Our birthday child was flushed with pleasure and happiness over everything, delighted that her birthday was the first one to be celebrated at Fruitlands. Lizzie was a favorite with us all, for hers was an outgoing sunny nature. Even on days when Louisa happened to be in one of her black moods, she never got irritated with Elizabeth. Instead Lizzie always seemed to comfort and cheer her.

Meanwhile Joseph Palmer had arrived at the farm. "As soon as I could get out of Worcester jail," he explained, stroking his famous beard. He brought with him a cartload of fine old furniture and implements and tools. An ardent antislavery advocate, eccentric but steadfast, he became one of the pillars of Fruitlands. His practical experience as a farmer guided us around more than one pitfall.

From the beginning we had so many visitors that it was hard to get the farm work done. Mr. Lane and my husband were always eager to talk about the aims of community life, and plans for the future, and to philosophize. Special work might be waiting to be done, but the philosophizing went on. Even Louisa noticed it. Once when I sent her to find out whether the men had stopped speculating and started on some urgent task, she reported with a sigh, "No, Marmee, they've begun again!"

As for me, visitors meant extra work in the kitchen and left me little time to enjoy them. When William Russell came from Andover, where he was prospering as a teacher, and when Mr. Ripley came from Brook Farm, I scarcely had time to greet them properly. I felt harassed, too, the day Brother Sam came with his family.

When Mr. Emerson visited us, I managed to steal a

few minutes with him. He brought greetings from Henry Thoreau who was at Staten Island, New York, that summer, tutoring the children of Mr. Emerson's brother. Then he asked how things were going at Fruitlands. I could sense at once that he still had doubts about the enterprise. "Have your husband and Mr. Lane sprouted wings yet?" he asked with a smile. Then, more seriously, "I think they might do better to acquire some cowhide boots."

"How do *you* think things look, Mr. Emerson?" I asked.

"Well enough . . . in July," he answered. "But what farm doesn't? I'll hold off my judgment until December."

December! I shivered at the thought of the cold winds of winter and the drafty house. Yes, I thought, December will be the crucial month.

Mr. Alcott and Mr. Lane felt that they must keep making talks at different places, to spread the Fruitlands gospel and get needed recruits for the community. I not only worried about the crops they neglected by their trips—crops that needed special attention because of late planting—but I also worried about my husband becoming a laughingstock in the outlandish outfit he wore.

They would start out, heads held high under their wide-brimmed hats, wearing trousers and tunics of brown linen flapping in the breeze. Mr. Lane forbade woollen clothes because that meant robbing sheep of their wool. He banished cotton, too, since it was a product of slave labor. He designed a queer linen outfit for all members of the community to wear, which was all right for the farm, but I shrank from the thought of raised eyebrows in Boston, and my dignified husband being made the butt of ridicule.

During the weeks of summer, my great consolation was the joy the children took in living in the country. I felt as if I could fold my arms around them all and say from the bottom of my heart, "My world is within my embrace." They loved to get up at five in the morning, with the rest of us. After their cold baths and breakfast, and helping with the work, they would run on the hill until time for their lessons.

Sometimes Louisa would tell me that she had "thoughts" when alone on the hill. "I sat and heard the pines sing a long time." Or she would tell me how the moon came up when she was in bed, and looked at her. At other times she would admit that even a run on the hill had not cheered her because she had been cross and disobedient.

On Abba May's third birthday near the end of July, she found her presents in a stocking we had filled for her. They were simple homemade things, but each little gift made our three-year-old dance with delight.

During the summer, in addition to their other tasks, the older girls and Willy Lane had wild berries to pick —mostly blueberries and blackberries. They were a welcome addition to our diet. The children made a game of picking: Who could find the most? So instead of coming home tired, they were always exhilarated. Knowing that the life at Fruitlands kept the girls healthy and happy, I found courage to bear up under the work that proved to be almost too much for my strength.

One of my constant worries was about food for the winter. How would there be enough, with the late planting and all? And how could we ever expect a good crop with Mr. Lane's queer notions of farming?

My doubts were reinforced by grumblings from Joseph Palmer. After an argument with Mr. Lane, I heard him urge one day: "What this land needs is some manure for fertilizer."

"We'll have nothing like that here," Mr. Lane replied sternly. "The very thought of it disgusts me. We can plow under some of our crops for fertilizer."

Another time when Joseph Palmer suggested that we plant some turnips, Mr. Lane objected. "Root crops that grow below the ground in the dark away from the sun are not fit food for our community." When Mr. Palmer told me this, we both had to laugh at Mr. Lane's inconsistency, since we had two acres planted to potatoes, as well as some rows of carrots.

Mr. Palmer grumbled at another of Mr. Lane's queer notions—that animals should not be enslaved and forced to plow the land. "If we're right-minded farmers," he insisted, "we should be willing to use spades to turn over the soil." Luckily Mr. Palmer had better sense and was not to be intimidated. After a short trial with the spade, he went back to the farm-stead his wife kept going and brought a plow and yoke of oxen to Fruitlands. Mr. Lane made no further objections about enslaving animals; in fact he was heard to complain that there was still too much hard manual labor to be done and too few men to help.

I had to take a stand against another of Mr. Lane's impractical ideas. My eyes were rebelling because of the nightly mending of endless garments by the dim light of bayberry candles. One night I burst out during a philosophical discussion to say, "You and your precious animals! I can't manage any longer without a whale-oil lamp."

Mr. Lane looked at me sternly. "There will be no animal oil burned here."

In a burst of temper I threw down my mending. "Then there will be no mending done here either." I flounced out of the room and kept my threat, sitting with folded hands the next few nights. Within the week someone brought a small lamp to Fruitlands for my use, and Mr. Lane had to forget his scruples against burning whale oil on the place.

I had to give him credit though for appreciating the hard work my husband did. He admired the efficient way Mr. Alcott guided the plow hour after hour, sometimes for the whole day. And he credited him with doing "a thousand things" in a day. But that, of course, was when he was there to do it.

When the two Minds of Fruitlands went off on one of their trips late in July, I had to leave the kitchen to help in the fields with the haying. Actually I enjoyed the change, raking the hay and helping to shock it. And it gave me a chance to thank Abraham Everett by action instead of words for all the help he had given me in the kitchen.

Toward the end of August I made a visit to the Shaker Community on the Nashua River near Fruitlands. I had so often heard Mr. Lane speak approvingly of the colony, in contrast to the way Fruitlands was turning out, that I wanted to see for myself. I had to admit that the Shakers' fields and crops and garden and orchard looked thriving, and their buildings were in excellent repair. But I felt that there was servitude somewhere, and I sensed that the yoke fell on the women. I saw no hope or serenity in any of their faces, not even resignation. The women had a cowed, almost resentful look, while the men looked fat, sleek and comfortable.

September came. As soon as the barley was cut and shocked, Mr. Lane and my husband started off again to Boston and Brook Farm to conduct Conversations. They hoped to earn a little money or bring back recruits, or possibly both. "Just a few days, Abba," Mr. Alcott assured me. "But in case we are delayed, have the men get the barley under cover if it looks like rain. That barley is our mainstay for the winter."

The very afternoon of their departure the sky clouded over and an easterly storm threatened. I sent the children running in all directions to tell the men to start bringing in the barley.

One by one the children returned with the report that they could find no men. "I saw the two beards start out early this morning for a Come-Outers meeting," Louisa reported.

"Some of the others must have gone with them," Anna said. "Or maybe they just went home."

The sky looked more threatening by the moment. "Then it's up to us to save the barley," I cried. "Willy, Anna, Louy, take the clothesbaskets to the field and begin to fill them. Lizzie and I will come with some old sheets and blankets and rope. Let's see how much barley we can get under cover before the rain begins."

How we worked, dragging the barley bundles to the barn in our improvised receptacles! Thunder rumbled. Lightning flashed. The wind buffeted us. But we all felt a wonderful exhilaration, working together against time.

"Isn't it *fun*, Marmee!" Louisa called out, as she and Willy passed me, dragging their overloaded clothesbasket. She was flushed and excited, her hair running wild.

Yes, it was fun, I had to admit. I had been washing all morning, bending over the tubs, but my weariness left me as I caught the children's spirit of adventure. Back and forth we went from field to barn, breathless, eager, putting every ounce of strength we had into the task. By the time the storm broke, we had saved most of the crop, and I knew that for all of us it was probably the high point of the summer.

CHAPTER 13

IN OCTOBER WE CELEBRATED another birthday, my own this time, my forty-third. The years seemed to weigh heavily on me, heavier than ever before. The prospect of Fruitlands in winter, with few supplies ahead and no money coming in, sent a chill through me.

Louisa was the first to run to me that morning with a birthday kiss. She had made me a cross out of moss, and I thought how appropriate it was, for I did indeed seem to be carrying a cross. Best of all, she had written me a poem.

My birthday came on Sunday, when no lessons were scheduled, and so we all went to the woods to play and gather red leaves. Anna made me a crown of oak leaves and decorated it with late-blooming flowers. Elizabeth, too, had made a little gift for me. The girls' love and enthusiasm and their father's festive spirit quickly engulfed me. Before the morning was half over, I promised myself I would never again let my years weigh me down.

The promise was easy enough to keep when I was with the children. It always surprised me to see how quickly much of our work turned into play. Like the corn-husking that came a few days after my birthday. We all went to the barn to husk corn, and it could have been a great chore. But we sang and told stories as we worked, and occasionally I sent the children on a run around the barn or a climb to the loft to take the kinks out of their legs. Dusk came and we were still far from finished. We kept on working by lantern light, with mysterious shadows slanting across the barn floor, and Louisa spoke for us all when the last ear was husked. "Let's do it again!"

But all too soon I let trouble weigh me down once more. I realized that Mr. Lane was putting pressure on my husband, trying to convince him to join the Shakers. Their community prospered, he argued, and was well-established, having survived the test of more than sixty years. Fruitlands, on the other hand, was not developing as it should. The Shakers' belief in celibacy appealed to Mr. Lane. He insisted that a man's wife and family interfered with his spiritual development. At the Shaker community men and women lived in separate buildings; and so did the children of the recruits and orphans the Government turned over to the Shakers to bring up.

As the weeks passed I became frightened, even terrified, to think of the effect of Mr. Lane's words on my husband. Did Bronson Alcott have the stamina to stand up and declare his love for his family, to declare how impossible a separation would be? Or would he really entertain the thought of giving up his family to follow Lane? Doubt and fear filled my days.

Early in November Willy Lane took sick and was confined to his bed for weeks, nursed by his moody father. How gladly I would have attended Willy myself without having to endure the exacting Mr. Lane underfoot!

Anyone could see that the New Eden had been a miserable failure. All the recruits had left except Joseph Palmer, and he expected to be on his way soon. He liked Fruitlands, though, and saw possibilities in it. More than once he suggested to Mr. Lane that he would be willing to buy it. Eventually that is what he did. He brought his wife and turned the place into a sort of goodwill farmstead. For years the Palmers kept an iron pot of beans and a pot of potatoes on the stove for anyone who might be hungry. And so in their strange way they managed to carry on the basic goodness that had led to the founding of Fruitlands.

I summoned all my reserve of good nature to make the 29th of November a happy day that year. Louy was eleven years old, and her father four times eleven. We had presents—simple ones that made up in imagination and love for what they lacked in money value. Then the children ran out eagerly to play before their lessons. The weather had turned cold and snow covered the ground. From the window I watched Louisa with barrel stays tied to her feet for runners. I was grateful that the girls could have carefree fun in spite of everything, and soon I was laughing myself at the ludicrous tumble she took.

By December I felt that things were coming to a head. We could not go on through the winter at Fruitlands. My Brother Sam wrote that he had rooms for me and the girls if I wanted to come. Yet I could not face being the one to make the break. In spite of everything, I loved Bronson Alcott. Though I sometimes lost my temper and patience with him, I still thought him the greatest, most idealistic man I knew. I had confidence that his own nature would soon break through and dispel the mesmerism of Mr. Lane.

Willy's health improved so much by the first week in December that Mr. Lane went off to Boston "on business." I decided that this was my chance to take a firm stand. One night after little Abba May and Elizabeth were in bed, and convalescing Willy sound asleep, we older Alcotts had a heart-to-heart talk in front of the grate. I felt that Anna and Louisa were mature enough to take part in the family council, and I knew that one of my husband's basic principles of education was that children had minds of their own. The time had come to place ideas about the sacredness of the family against Mr. Lane's disruptive theories.

We talked for a long time. At the mere mention of breaking up the family, Anna and Louisa began to cry. Soon I was crying, too, and so was my husband. We decided that about all we had of any value was each other. None of us could face the prospect of separation. Louisa whispered to me when she said good-night that she would pray to God to keep us together.

With Mr. Lane away, our family ties grew even tighter as unusually bitter weather descended upon our hilltop. We felt as if we were isolated on a tiny island in the midst of the raging sea of winter. Most of our energy went into mere survival, making our way to the barn for wood, and stringing out our small stock of provisions.

As Christmas approached I wondered what I could do to make the day merry for the children. Snow was banked deep around the house; our meager supply of food offered nothing in the way of treats. Never before had we used such ingenuity in making gifts. The day turned out to be a festive one in spite of everything. We asked some of the neighbors' children to come in the evening for singing, games, and merrymaking . . . and no one seemed to miss the sugar plums.

Finally my husband must have told Mr. Lane that he would not leave his family, for early in January Mr. Lane went off with Willy to join the Shakers. I felt that now all would be well with us. But no. Mr. Alcott was so physically exhausted from the labor of trying to make Fruitlands productive, and so filled with despair and discouragement over the failure of the project, that he became acutely ill. A sense of utter defeat swept over him, a defeat even more engulfing than the failure of Temple School had brought on. He seemed to have no heart to go on living.

For days and days he lay in bed, refusing food and drink. Severe cold kept hemming us in. In the mornings I had to take a hammer to break the ice on the water pail. The girls and I had difficulty keeping the fires going and the paths shoveled. All this time Mr. Alcott lay with his face to the wall. I could do nothing except try to comfort him. I kept telling him that the only failure is for a man to be ruined, dwarfed by his idea . . . that success is profiting by one's mistakes and growing through them.

I kept food and fresh water within reach, hoping against hope that he would want them. But he lay there in silence. I had a feeling that he was waiting for death to release him. My heart went out to him, but I knew that he alone could work out his problem.

Finally, somehow, he realized that it was life he wanted, not death. It was his family he wanted, not the visionary schemes of Mr. Lane. He turned his face to me with a wan smile and held out his hand with words I shall never forget: "My faithful wife, my little girls, they have not forsaken me, they are mine by ties that none can break. What right have I to leave them alone? What right to escape from the burden and the sorrow I have helped to bring?"

The battle was won. It was his family he wanted, though he had had to come close to the brink of death to be sure. At last the terrible strain of those days and nights, like the weight of a mountain, lifted from my shoulders. He had said we were his by ties that none could break. After that I could face anything again . . . poverty, hunger, cold, yes, even ridicule, so long as we were together.

Never was I so glad to move as I was when we left Fruitlands behind us forever. In mid-January we moved to our neighbor Lovejoy's, where we rented three rooms and the use of the kitchen for fifty cents a week. The quarters were far more comfortable than the drafty rooms at Fruitlands.

We had practically no money to live on. Mr. Alcott was in no condition to carry on Conversations, and besides the weather was too severe for him to be out on the snowy roads. Brother Sam, sensing our need as usual, enclosed ten dollars in a letter. I took stock of our resources. There was the prized silver dish that had gone with us from house to house for almost fourteen years. A cousin had written me once that any time I felt I could part with the dish, she would pay ten dollars for it.

Resolutely I shined the wedding-present dish for the last time, wrapped it after the girls were in bed, and sent it to the post office the next morning with Mr.

Lovejoy. No one would ever know my regret at having to sell it. But I was sure that Hannah Robie, the well-loved donor, would not think badly of me for parting with it under the circumstances.

I still had a good cloak that I was able to sell to a friend for twelve dollars. And I managed to get some sewing to do in the nearby village of Still River. And so one way or another we managed to get through the winter.

Not knowing what course to take for the future, we decided to look over other communities where members were trying to live what they believed to be an ideal life. But we found that none of them gave any real promise of the sort of life we wanted, a life centered around our children. Brook Farm, by far the largest, with well over a hundred participants, impressed us as being better than any of the others. It was neater and more orderly, with more emphasis on beauty. But even it had little to offer us.

So, after an unusually cold winter at Lovejoy's, we moved to the village of Still River, a tiny crossroads settlement nearby. There, renting half a house and a garden plot, we hoped to produce abundant food, spiritual as well as material. At once my husband began to lay out a garden. He worked at it so faithfully and well that in a short time the change in the place was unbelievable. Soon we had early lettuce, radishes, and onions to eat, and the girls found dandelion greens in abundance. And being right in the village, I found it easier to get sewing to do.

I look back with special pleasure on the months we lived in Still River. We were able to sink our roots down into normal living again, just our own family once more. No more baggy trousers and long tunics of brown linen, no more arguments about vegetables that grew above ground or underground! The girls had other children to play with, and for the first time they went to the district school. I felt that they needed the association with other children in regular classes for a change. They thrived on it. On sunny days boys and girls gathered on the grass plot in front of our house to play ball, jump rope, and play games. I sat at the window with my sewing, my heart full of joy to have so much life and high spirits around me.

With only four rooms in our half of "Brickends," as the house was called, a living room and kitchen downstairs and two bedrooms upstairs, we could not have existed on rainy days without the woodshed for a playhouse. There the girls and their friends had no trouble entertaining themselves and me, too, when I had time to join them. I never knew where Anna's and Louy's imaginations would lead them . . . and their playmates looked to them for an uninterrupted flow of ideas.

One day I witnessed a wedding. Louisa, wearing one of my old white aprons for a wedding veil, became the bride of Walter Gardner who lived across the way. Another boy, acting the minister, pronounced them man and wife after they exchanged solemn vows "until death do us part." But in two minutes they disagreed about something, tempers flared up, Louy slapped the groom, and they parted. Soon they were acting out parts from *As You Like It* and everyone was in good humor again.

At Still River, Louisa, no longer held in check by a disciplinarian like Mr. Lane, almost ran wild for a time. I tried not to let it worry me, realizing it was probably only a normal reaction. She developed into quite a tease, sparing only quiet Elizabeth, and always seemed to be getting into scrapes. One night she took to lighting matches, and because of the fire risk her father thought it necessary to spank her, something that happened very rarely. The mortifying experience calmed our impetuous girl temporarily.

Her temper continued to be a problem, but sometimes she managed to work it off harmlessly and ingeniously. Once when she was cleaning the house in a swirl of energy she crashed into a chair, receiving quite a hard bump. Immediately her temper exploded. She kicked the chair, only to get a more painful injury. After she calmed down, she decided to put the chair on trial, acting as complainant, judge, and jury all in one. Later when I saw the chair dangling outside the bedroom window on a rope and asked for an explanation, she said, "I put it on trial for bumping me, and found it guilty, and condemned it to be hanged."

For all the girls those months in Still River were full of great good times. Later Louisa told me that it was the happiest summer she ever spent in the country.

The playacting the girls had started at the Hosmer cottage developed and expanded at Still River. In this Anna and Louisa took after me. When I was their age my fondest wish was to become an actress, though, of course, my family would have none of it. My interest in the theater never waned, even when the stage was one end of the woodshed; and I always had time, no matter how many other tasks had to be postponed, to help the girls with their costumes and stage sets.

Mr. Alcott seemed to enjoy his Still River summer, too. The long hours he spent in his garden and at woodchopping he balanced off with equally long hours at his desk, reading and writing. Several more of his papers had been published in *The Dial*, which Mr. Emerson had been editing since 1842. I was hopeful that this would continue to be an outlet for my husband's thoughts, although I knew the magazine was having a hard time financially. So it was with disappointment but not surprise that we learned there would be no summer issue of *The Dial* in that year of 1844. Its life was over.

But news of new life of a different kind brought us joy that summer. A son was born to the Emersons, Edward Waldo, two and a half years after the death of the beloved Waldo.

We Alcotts had good fortune too that summer in meeting a boy who turned out to be almost a son to us. Strange, how some chance meetings are ships that pass in the night, while others ripen into real friendship, like my meeting with Llewellyn Willis.

One day, coming home from Boston on the stage-coach, I happened to sit next to Llewellyn. He had an alert face, and seemed to be about Anna's age, perhaps a little older. After one of the stops, the driver slammed the heavy door shut on the boy's hand. The pain was so severe the lad fainted. I held him in my arms while we worked to help him regain conscious-ness. He told me afterward how much it meant to him to find a motherly-looking face leaning over him when he opened his eyes.

After bandaging his crushed fingers, I encouraged him to tell about himself.

"I'm an orphan," he explained, "living with my grandparents. In the summer my grandfather likes to send me to board in the country. Last summer I was at the village of Harvard. This year I am bound for Still River."

"How strange!" I exclaimed. "Last summer we lived near Harvard, and this year we are at Still River." I looked at his sensitive face questioningly. "Did you perhaps hear of Fruitlands?"

"Oh, indeed. I heard so much about the 'strange people' there that I wanted to go see for myself. A young woman I knew promised to take me, but at the last minute she couldn't find her gloves and she said it would be impossible to go without them."

I burst into laughter. "Gloves! That would have been the final touch for us at Fruitlands."

"You were there?" He hesitated, then burst out suddenly. "Then could you be Mrs. Alcott?" My nod made him flush. "I heard so much about you and your daughters . . . but not that *you* were strange people."

Llewellyn quite forgot the pain in his hand when I told him about Anna and Louy and the two younger girls, told about the games they played and the dramas they put on. I made him promise to come see us the very next day.

He did, and we all got along so famously that soon afterward Llewellyn left his boarding place and came to live with us for the summer. I was glad, of course, for the small income it brought in, but even more glad to have such a delightful boy as part of the family. For the next ten years, while he was still in school and college, he lived with us for part of each year.

Had our own boy lived, I would have wanted him to be like Llewellyn. What a brother he was to the girls, entering into all their fun in such a high-spirited way! And so responsible always. I would send them off for the day with lunch basket, wraps, and storybooks piled in a little four-wheeled cart, and they would make a fairyland out of a grove near a favorite pond. There they would play the parts of a royal family, with Anna the dignified queen, Llewellyn the king, and Louisa the high-spirited princess. Little did the royal family, unpacking their lunch basket, realize how empty the larder was at home, how precarious our footing as we crossed the bridge of summer to the more demanding weeks of fall and winter.

CHAPTER 14

WE HAD KNOWN ALL ALONG that our stay in Still River
was to be only temporary. Mr. Alcott liked plain living
but that alone was not enough. He wanted high thinking too, and the kind of companionship he had in
Concord with friends like Mr. Emerson and Henry
Thoreau. For Bronson Alcott food for the mind was
more important than food for the body, and always
would be. I, too, missed what Concord had to offer.
Surely, we decided, there would be as many hems to
sew and as much wood to chop in Concord as in Still
River.

Besides, I had recently learned from my cousins and
my brother that we could use the money from my
legacy to buy a home of our own, providing it would
never be mortgaged. It was obvious that my father

wanted to protect us from going further into debt.

I worried continually about our debts. They oppressed me much more than they did Mr. Alcott, who had an abiding faith that someday, somehow, they would be paid. I could never quite figure out how. But in the meantime I felt it would be wonderful for the girls to have the security of living in a home of our own. I was sure we would have my father's blessing in moving back to Concord and finding a house.

We made the move early in November, taking rooms with the Edmund Hosmer family until we could find the house we wanted. Within a few weeks we found it—an old place on the Lexington road, the road down which Paul Revere had ridden on that historic April night in 1775. It was not far from Emersons' and less than a mile and a half from the center of Concord. Louisa thought it very amusing that our "new house" was almost 150 years old, and she made fun of the crooked doors and cupboards, the steps from one level to another, and the big knots poking up from the floor boards.

The old place, which had been owned by a farmer who raised hogs in the front yard, was badly in need of repairs. My husband assured me that he could put it into just the right shape to meet our needs. The house was rectangular, of two stories, with a great chimney in the center. Downstairs a hallway opened onto two large rooms in front and a lean-to in the rear, where there was another chimney. Upstairs to my great relief there were two large bedrooms. For the first time we would have a chance to spread out a little, although for a while the girls would have to put up with two double beds in the bigger bedroom.

I was glad the house faced the south, for a southern exposure had always seemed best to me. But I shook my head over the condition of the yard. It was barren and almost treeless, the soil so sandy and gravelly I doubted if even my husband could make it bloom.

Mr. Alcott never worked so hard as at "Hillside," our name for the place. With Mr. Hosmer's help, he cut an old Wheelwright's shop in two and used the sections for wings on the house. This gave us a study and other small rooms, to say nothing of a bathhouse and woodshed.

Mr. Emerson caught some of my husband's dream and bought eight acres across the road for us to beautify and use. The land contained an unsightly barn which Mr. Alcott at once removed, giving us a sweeping view of countryside. Beyond Bister's Hill, across the road from us, lay Walden Pond where Mr. Emerson owned some land. At the time we were moving into Hillside, Henry Thoreau, with Mr. Emerson's blessings, was cutting trees and hewing timbers at the Pond, preparing to build a hut. He planned to live alone there while writing a book. My husband was delighted and said, "It will make a nice walk for me of a Sunday evening in winter, Abba."

Hillside was much to my liking, especially as Mr.

Alcott added improvements. By the first of April, 1845, we were able to move in, though the work was far from finished. All spring, summer, and fall my husband kept busy carrying out his plans for the house and grounds. So occupied was he with carpentering, gardening, tree-planting, landscaping, and terracing that he rarely stopped to talk, not even with Mr. Emerson or Henry Thoreau. And as for writing in his Journal that year, he was content to make the scantiest entries.

For a man so gifted intellectually, my husband was unusually clever with his hands. A saw, hammer and chisel, spade, mattock and hoe were congenial companions. He added a porch at the front of the house which greatly improved its appearance. He spaded all the ground, adding black soil for enrichment. Then he made winding paths and planted shrubs and trees. At the back of the house he terraced the long sandy hillside and planted more trees. He worked like a man possessed. By the end of the summer he had effected such a transformation that people began to say we had one of the most picturesque places in Concord.

My province was the inside of the house, and I worked hard to make it cheery and homelike. We had chintz curtains in the old-fashioned parlor, and a cool inexpensive matting on the floor. A few fine engravings left over from Temple School hung on the walls. At last there was room to place the busts of the great men effectively, and the many books we had accumulated. The potted plants in the windows were the special care and joy of Elizabeth who watered them faithfully and gloried in every new blossom.

We still had some good heavy pieces of walnut and mahogany furniture and a piano that had belonged to the May family, and although they were rather scratched and nicked from frequent moving, they responded to care. Louisa was the first to notice that the silver dish did not appear on the sideboard in its usual place. I told her what had happened to it and pledged her to secrecy. Impetuously she threw her arms around me. "Oh, Marmee, some day I'm going to buy you a whole set of silver dishes . . . on a big silver tray, like Mrs. Emerson's. Someday I'm going to buy you anything you want."

I kissed her and told her that the thing I wanted most I already had—our family all together and happy.

A few weeks later when Louisa and I were working together in the kitchen I talked joyously of Hillside and how pleased I was about the way everything was turning out . . . the ample room we had, the new porch, the numerous doors leading to the outside. "It exceeds my fondest dreams!" I exclaimed.

"Not mine," Louisa replied quickly.

I looked at her wonderingly.

"Every night I pray for Papa to add something else. Every night I dream he does. But it never happens." With a deep sigh Louisa hung up the dishtowel. "How long can you keep wishing, Marmee, before it comes true?"

"Whatever are you talking about, Louy?"

"It doesn't have to be big . . . just so it's my own. A little room all of my own. Where I can keep my things, and write, and just sit and think, without anybody else being there."

"Someday," I promised her, "you shall have a room of your own. But aren't you a little young yet, not thirteen till November? Maybe next year . . . " I counseled patience and assured her that if the little room was necessary for her peace of mind, it would be hers before too long.

It was a busy time, but not too busy to help others. One day early in May my husband was out sharpening his axe before breakfast. He had much work to do on our house yet, but this was the day Henry Thoreau had set aside for the houseraising at Walden Pond. Mr. Emerson had promised to be there, and Ellery Channing, and Edmund Hosmer and his three sons, and Bronson Alcott with his trusty axe.

Although overburdened with work at Hillside, my husband looked forward to helping with the "hut," as Henry called it. "Henry is to have the cellar hole dug by the time we get there," he told me, "a hole six feet square and seven feet deep. By the end of the day we will have the frame of the house set over it, and the roof raised. Henry will finish it himself. He bought an old shanty for about four dollars and plans to use the boards for siding."

In June on Elizabeth's tenth birthday her father presented her with a pair of new shoes, a great event in the Alcott household, since our shoes were usually hand-me-downs from more affluent relatives. He bought them with money he had earned by helping a neighbor get in his hay before a storm broke, money I am sure he was tempted to use for a book he wanted. With the gift came a little note that I urged Lizzie to copy in her Journal: "I hope the shoes will fit your ready Feet as nicely as does your little Head the shape of your Mind."

Llewellyn came to stay with us at Hillside that first summer. The girls showed him all their old haunts around Concord, and together they discovered new ones. They had a merry time. On rainy days, or late in the afternoon on sunny days, we would gather in the parlor and Llewellyn would read to us while the girls and I sewed. We went back to *Philothea*, Maria Child's book about ancient Greece, because Anna and Louisa wanted to make a new and more elaborate dramatization. Llewellyn also read from Shakespeare, Scott, Dickens, or one of the English poets. Afterward we would talk over what he had read.

At the supper table Mr. Alcott would forget his work of the day and entertain us with a story, or he would talk of the wonders of nature around us, or give us a fascinating explanation of the growth and maturing of the apples or nuts we happened to be eating. He looked like an inspired philosopher, sitting there speaking gently and yet persuasively, with a ray of light occasionally slanting across his silvery hair. Though he was only forty-six years old, most of the traces of his blond hair were already gone.

Mr. Alcott's table talk especially delighted Llewellyn as did Mr. Alcott himself. One day when Llewellyn was helping me run the washing through the wringer, he said thoughtfully, "When I do physical work my thoughts run off in all directions. But it seems to me that Mr. Alcott is always a philosopher, no matter what he is doing. Somehow he doesn't seem to belong to today's world." I smiled and nodded, and Llewellyn went on, "He ought to be living back in the days of Socrates, wearing a flowing Greek robe. Or maybe in the days of Seneca in a Roman toga. It's hard to put into words the way I feel about him, because . . . because . . . "

"What, Llewellyn?"

"Because sometimes those very philosophical ways of his make me impatient. He's so impractical, Mrs. Alcott."

"An impractical idealist, is that what you mean?"

Llewellyn nodded.

"He is a wonderful man, Llewellyn. But if I send him for a pail of milk, like as not he'll come home with a cow." I laughed, and the dear boy, catching my eye, laughed too. How I wished that he were my son.

Then one rainy afternoon a strange thing happened during an intermission in our reading aloud. For some unremembered reason I mentioned the name of my brother-in-law in Boston, Benjamin Willis.

"Maybe he's related to me. Willis isn't such a common name," Llewellyn said.

Louisa pricked up her ears, sensing a dramatic situation. "Maybe you're our long lost cousin, Llewellyn!" she cried. "Maybe it was our fate all along to rescue you from being lonesome."

It turned out that Llewellyn and I were indeed distantly connected through my brother-in-law, a circumstance that was enough for all of us to treat our guest henceforth as a real cousin.

Louisa made the most of the discovery by insisting that we raise a flag in honor of the occasion. "And I'm going to write a play called 'The Long Lost Cousin,'" she declared, "and we'll put it on in the front yard under the trees and ask the Emersons and all the neighbors. But first we have to raise the flag."

This presented a problem, since we Alcotts had no flag. I probed the depths of a barrel of old clothes and produced an old red flannel skirt, some white muslin for stripes and stars, and a discarded blue cape for the field. Merrily we all set to work. "We'll need twenty-seven stars," Anna said, remembering that Florida had been admitted to the Union a few months before. "Marmee, how do you make the pattern for a star?"

The flag and the play were a great success, and Llewellyn became more than ever a member of the family and a star performer in Anna's and Louisa's theatrical productions.

In August I was dismayed to have Mr. Lane propose to spend a few weeks with us at Hillside before going back to England. I had fervently hoped never to see the man again, although I knew that he had entrusted his books to my husband's care. Disappointed in the Shaker community, Mr. Lane had withdrawn from it.

For some days I had a tussle with myself before I could graciously consent to Mr. Lane's visit. I tried to forget how close he had come to disrupting our family, and to remember instead that he had invested all his money in the Fruitlands venture, only to have it fail miserably. In many ways I could not help feeling sorry for him. Yet the idea of having him in our home again filled me with anxiety. Would he try once more to influence Mr. Alcott?

My worry turned out to be needless. My husband was preoccupied with his work and plans for Hillside. He was an agreeable host, but no longer an eager disciple. The visit went off pleasantly enough, and in my heart I was gratified that we could all part friends, though I had little desire to see him again.

Not long after Mr. Lane's departure, we had another guest from England, the distinguished Robert Owen, whom my husband thought very highly of. I knew about him, of course, from his social reforms in England and his New Harmony experiment in Indiana. Again I was apprehensive about the effect of the visit on Mr. Alcott, although Mr. Owen would be staying only two or three days. Was the failure of

Fruitlands truly a thing of the past? Or were my husband's dreams of community living ready to light up again under the influence of a man like Robert Owen?

It was a relief to know that we would not be entertaining Mr. Owen alone, but that Mr. Emerson would be with us for long sessions of talk. Mr. Emerson had never been swept off his feet by any of the community projects.

We had a large party for Robert Owen, and it turned out to be a highly successful evening. Our guests, unfeasted and untoasted, left, I hope, with the feeling that love and intelligence were the best hospitality.

Mr. Owen's love for mankind and his kindly allowance for human failings impressed all of us. But he failed to convince us that character is determined wholly by environment. He believed that the wrongdoing of men would disappear in a self-supporting community where the environment was favorable for right living.

I was glad to have Mr. Emerson point out that such things as living for show, and also poverty of vital power, could appear in a community project as well as anywhere else. Quickly I glanced at my husband. He was nodding in agreement. Then I knew that the lessons of Fruitlands did not have to be learned over again. He could admire Robert Owen without wanting to put his idealism to the test. Silently, I gave thanks.

CHAPTER 15

THE BIG EVENT FOR LOUISA came in March the next year, when she was thirteen years old. Her dream of having a room of her own came true. With the arrival of spring her father went to considerable pains to make one of the small rooms downstairs in the west wing comfortable for her.

With a happy pen Louisa wrote about it in her Journal:

"I have at last got the little room I have wanted so long, and am very happy about it. It does me good to be alone, and Mother has made it very pretty and neat for me. My work-basket and desk are by the window, and my closet is full of dried herbs that smell very nice. The door that opens into the garden will be very pretty in summer, and I can run off to the woods when I like."

Mr. Alcott continued to make improvements at Hillside. He devised an ingenious shower for our cold baths, rigging it up with weights and pulleys so that even Elizabeth could give herself a bath without help. After cleaning out the well and having it stoned, he ran a pipe into the kitchen and installed a pump at the iron sink. He brought trees from Walden Wood —pines, hemlocks, maples, and birches and planted them on the grounds. In the garden he cut an attractive semicircular walk, setting out apple trees nearby. I was glad to help him with the transplanting. The girls came to watch, and we all felt a joyful participation in this work of hope and promise on land that belonged to us.

Although we always made it a practice to observe May Day, when new life was springing up after the cold and dark of winter, that year we made a special occasion of it. The girls filled their May baskets as usual with a profusion of wildflowers—spring beauties, violets, wood anemones, hepaticas, triliums. Then we prepared for our joint celebration of the day with the Emersons on their lawn. Although Ellen Emerson was only seven years old, and Edith and Edward younger than our youngest, all our girls enjoyed the Emerson children. And they in turn enjoyed our girls. Louisa was their favorite storyteller, a role which she both enjoyed and took seriously. Miss Sophia Ford was tutoring the Emerson children that year, as well as the Alcotts and Channings, in a schoolroom in the Emerson barn. She was a woman of ideas, ever suggesting interesting things to do.

On May Day morning Miss Ford came over with Ellen and we all had a good time putting colored streamers on the Maypole my husband had supplied, and decorating it with evergreens. Mr. Alcott had brought a load of trees from the woods for decorations and trimmed a borrowed haycart with pine boughs. The girls made wreaths of pine for our hats, and Elizabeth and Ellen found violets for us all to wear.

Finally, while the morning was still young, we rode over to Emersons' in the haycart, singing "Merrily we go!" as we jounced along the road. Some of the neighborhood mothers and children joined us on the lawn, and the boys and girls danced around the Maypole, singing as they danced.

While the children were dancing, Mr. Alcott took my arm and swung me around gaily with a cheery "Merrily we go!"

"At my age!" I gasped, laughing.

"At any age, Abba," he replied. "Look at Miss Ford, flushed as a schoolgirl."

Miss Ford provided Louisa with a great deal of pleasure and amusement that summer. She treasured little happenings to tell me about, things that came up on their nature walks. Once she swore me to secrecy, lest Miss Ford's reputation be hurt among some of the staid villagers. "Now remember, don't tell, Mother! But imagine us wading across a big pond a mile long . . . carrying our shoes and stockings and picking up our skirts at the same time . . . scaring the fishes and making them swim like mad. And then the funny time we had on the other side, getting our shoes and stockings on again. If you wonder why my dress is muddy, that's why. Miss Ford's was worse. But we all came home singing and laughing."

Though they were getting older the girls still loved the out-of-doors. I sometimes feared that they made themselves a nuisance when they walked to Walden Pond to see Mr. Thoreau. Henry had moved there to pursue his studies of nature and to have time to write, not to entertain a stream of visitors. I mentioned my anxiety to him one afternoon when he stopped to pick up a book my husband had promised him.

He gave me one of his rare engaging smiles. "I like children who show an interest in nature. That means the Alcott girls. I like their informality. Like to see them surprised by some of the secrets around them."

"I understand that you can whistle like a bird, and imitate the calls of animals. And the things you tell about fish, fowl, and ferret are much more fascinating than fairy tales. But I don't want the children to bother you," I said.

"I save some of the rare things for them to see,

Mrs. Alcott. So I'd be disappointed if they didn't come."

We all looked forward to those evenings when Henry could be persuaded to eat supper with us. Afterward we would sit around the fire, the older girls and I with our work-baskets, and listen to his tales of the Concord of his boyhood, tales as engrossing to Bronson Alcott and me as to little Abba.

Henry Thoreau and our Abba May had a great joke, continued from one meeting to the next. He would cut an apple in half with such a fine line that the break scarcely showed. Then Abba would ask her father to crack the apple for her. It would fall apart in his hands! But sometimes Henry would get Abba to hand her father an uncut apple, which he expected to fall apart. When it didn't we all burst out laughing.

Occasionally Mr. Thoreau would take his flute from his pocket and treat us to some of his music. He could play so gently and melodiously that I could well believe tales that he was the Pied Piper of Walden, summoning the wild creatures to him. Elizabeth, our musical daughter, was particularly entranced by his playing. One evening Henry taught her to play a few simple tunes in a very short time. He told me as he left that I had a gifted daughter, and I decided then and there that no matter how many additional economies I had to effect, I would see to it that Elizabeth kept on with her piano lessons.

One quickly forgot about Henry Thoreau's big

hooked nose and weathered outdoor complexion when he shared his knowledge of nature. But there was always one drawback to his visits. None of the children ever wanted to go to bed!

Our Fourth of July that second summer at Hillside was almost as memorable as May Day had been. We Alcotts walked to Walden Pond with the picnic basket, to share our meal with Henry Thoreau. He had been living in his hut just a year, enjoying and observing the wonders of nature around him, and working on the manuscript of *A Week on the Concord and the Merrimack Rivers*, a trip which he had taken with his brother John seven years before. The five children, for Llewellyn was with us, started out noisily, laughing and talking as they went along. But as soon as we neared the Pond they quieted down of their own accord, even tomboy Louisa.

Mr. Thoreau greeted us graciously and had us come into his little house. At once he began talking to Mr. Alcott about some wildflowers he had seen in Walden Wood. Then he turned to the rest of us. "Can you keep very, very still? As if you were part of the shadow in my house?"

Eager nods from the children made me realize that this was not the first time they had been sworn to stillness.

Quietly Henry stepped outside the door. After a pause, during which we were so quiet we could hear our hearts tick, he gave a strange low whistle. Almost

at once a woodchuck popped out of his hole and began running toward him. Mr. Thoreau gave a different kind of low whistle, and a pair of gray squirrels
scampered down a tree and ran towards him without
fear. Another call brought two crows out of the woods
to rest on his shoulder.

Watching from the shadows of the hut, we were en-
chanted to see our host reach into his pocket for food
for all of them. They took it from his hand.

"One of my favorite friends is a mouse with a nest
under the house," he told us later. "She keeps my floor
free of crumbs. But when she wants a more substantial
dinner, she comes right into my hands. Afterwards, she
lets me watch her clean her face and paws. Any time
I'm lonesome of an evening, I just call her with my
flute."

During Henry Thoreau's second year at Walden
Pond, he and Mr. Alcott were close companions. The
pressure of carpentry work at Hillside was over, and
during the cold months nothing could be done in the
yard and garden. And so on many a wintry afternoon
or evening my husband would walk over to the Pond
for a visit. That Henry looked forward to these visits
I had no doubt. "Your husband," he told me once, "is
almost alone among my friends with whom I can express my most cherished fancies and thoughts at my
leisure without any obstacles in the way."

In many ways Henry seemed almost like a son of
Bronson Alcott, I thought, as I watched him start out

through the snow. They were both so unconcerned with the material things of this world. Henry had proved in his father's pencil factory that he could make a pencil equal to the best ones manufactured in London. Yet rather than make a big business out of his father's little family factory, he preferred to pursue his studies of nature without a dollar in his pocket. More than anything else, he believed in the art of living, just as Bronson Alcott did.

Neither man was ever idle. Henry turned his hand to almost any kind of manual labor when he needed money to tide him over. Of course, as a single man, his needs were few compared to the family responsibilities resting on my husband's shoulders. Yet neither man was willing to do anything to earn money unless the work gave him satisfaction in the doing. Neither had any talent for making money, or keeping it, which of course made them ne'er-do-wells in the eyes of many of the villagers.

Neither was self-indulgent in food or drink. Alcohol was not for them, nor tobacco either. Both were vegetarians and ate sparingly of the simplest foods. Mr. Emerson laughingly told me once that he asked Henry at dinner what dish he preferred. The reply came quickly. "The nearest."

There was another similarity between Henry and my husband. Both knew how to be poor in a dignified way that lent a certain grace to poverty. Lack of money never weighed them down. It had no connection with the soaring of their spirits, and, I must confess, I envied them this. In spite of empty pocketbooks, they always had something to share with others—ideas, a gracious welcome, a book, a berry patch, a serenity of outlook.

Both men were idealists, first, last, and always. And though their idealism might show itself in different ways, come what may they clung to their high purposes.

Henry's mother, I am glad to say, appreciated her son's unique qualities quite as much as I appreciated my husband's. It was not always easy, but we both realized that every man had to work out his own destiny or he would cease to be himself. The life of the Thoreau family was as delightfully intimate as our own. It was a rich home life even though created out of the simplest materials.

The Hawthornes were another family with a full and happy home life in spite of genteel poverty. Nathaniel Hawthorne had stories within him that insisted on being written, but in those early days of his writing, he found it hard to find editors willing to pay more than a few dollars for a story. The Hawthornes had a good garden, and Sophia was able to earn a little money with her painting, and she was ever on the alert to get along with as little as possible. But the scarcity of money became a real problem for the Hawthornes after their first child, Una, was born in 1844. By the next year Mr. Hawthorne saw that it was impossible to live without some source of steady income, and so he moved his family to Salem and became surveyor of the port. But before he left he managed to put together a collection of his short stories which were published as *Mosses from an Old Manse*.

We read the book eagerly, of course, since the Old Manse was none other than the house where the Hawthornes had lived in Concord. My husband and I found the title sketch quite revealing in giving a side of Mr. Hawthorne we had known little about, his feeling that nature was an expression of spiritual truth.

November, the birthday month, was upon me before I realized it. I had little with which to buy gifts for Louisa and her father, and this year, Louy's fourteenth birthday, seemed to be such an important year in a girl's life. Childhood days were over, young womanhood ahead. What could I get that would be just right to fit the occasion?

Finally, with a smile, I wrapped a little present and wrote a poem to accompany it.

On the birthday morning Louisa flung her arms around me when she opened the small gift and read the poem. "My own room," she cried, "and now a new pen, and my head full of ideas!" She read my verse aloud to the family:

> "Oh, may this pen your muse insire,
> When wrapt in pure poetic fire . . ."

"Oh, I think this is the best birthday of all!"

CHAPTER 16

AFTER HER FOURTEENTH BIRTHDAY, Louisa tried harder than ever to curb her temper and shake off her moods. Having a room of her own where she could sit and think and write made more difference than I thought possible.

One of the first poems Louisa wrote with the new pen was on this very subject. She called it "My Kingdom," a long poem of thirty-two lines, which I thought read exceedingly well. I was surprised and delighted, for I had many a time read poems in the papers that did not come up to this standard. How well she summarized her theme in the last stanza!

> "*I do not ask for any crown*
> *But that which all may win,*

> *Nor seek to conquer any world*
> *Except the one within.*
> *Be thou my guide until I find,*
> *Led by a tender hand,*
> *Thy happy kingdom in* myself,
> *And dare to take command."*

Mr. Alcott and I were happy to think that both Louisa and Anna had a natural gift for writing. Their practice in collaborating on the plays that they produced and acted in, gave them a feeling for the dramatic in stories. Louisa had a further flair for the fanciful. If only, I often thought, their father had some of the girls' spontaneity and freedom in writing, if only he could write as naturally and easily as he could talk! His staid, scholarly style made his work formidable and hard to read, to say nothing of making it hard to sell.

Ever since Mr. Emerson had adversely criticized a manuscript of Mr. Alcott's years before, a manuscript on which months of toil had been lavished, my husband had resigned himself to the conviction that he could never succeed as a writer. Perhaps it was true. It did seem that words that flowed so fluently from my husband's lips became stilted as soon as he put them on paper.

His own lack of skill in writing did not in the least dull his pleasure in the girls' accomplishments. After reading "My Kingdom," he exclaimed, his face alight,

"It seems we have a poet in the family!"

I doubt if there ever lived a father more devoted to a family of girls. The boy in him was never too old to play with them, even though the man's hair was turning white. Often he entered into their games in the barn and in the house, and walked with them through fields and woods and up the hill. From their earliest childhood he read aloud to them—*Pilgrim's Progress* every year, and other books like the *Faerie Queene* whose inward meanings needed explaining. He habitually planned their dresses because he had greater talent for design than I. When the girls were ill, he helped to nurse them. He often cooked their meals. He gave them lessons and encouraged them in their work. With kindness but firmness he disciplined them. And in return, one and all, they loved him.

As the girls grew older, the differences between them became more pronounced. Anna, our dependable quiet one, inherited her father's patience and shyness. Louisa might scold and fume over a disappointment, but Anna would accept it philosophically, confident that everything would turn out all right. Like her father, she was tall, blonde, and graceful, and she always seemed to retain her dignity. Anna had another characteristic that ever endeared her to me. From earliest childhood she was like a little mother, watching over Louy—when Louy would let her—and later mothering Elizabeth and Abba May with unending warmth and love.

Of all our girls, Elizabeth was most like her father. If I had to put it in one word, I should say "lovable." She had an even, serene temperament and the same kind of deep religious feeling her father had. They both *lived* it. The rapport between the two of them was a delight to see. Lizzie's talent for music, though, came through the Mays. She loved music and played the piano well, and with expression. Though not as hardy as the others, she was a sunny child and filled a special niche in all our hearts.

Our Abba May, with her sparkling temperament, was the most social of the four. Being the baby, she was, I am afraid, somewhat spoiled. Her fair complexion, light wavy hair, and blue eyes made her an unusually attractive child, except when impulsiveness or impatience ruled her. Like Louisa and me, she had a quick temper . . . and a quick repentance. Abba, whom we soon were to call May at her request, inherited her father's artistic sensitiveness and manual skill, and was never happier than when she had crayon or paintbrush in her hand.

Louisa . . . what shall I say about Louisa, who was always big for her age both in mind and body? Above all, she was her mother's child in ways besides appearance and temperament. She had my energetic constitution and practical outlook on life, and, my husband always said, my wit and tenderness. Yet one characteristic of her father's she had more strongly than any of the girls—a complete dedication to her ideals. Because she was like me in so many ways, I understood her far better than her father did, and felt especially close to her. She might be difficult at times, but she was always my Louy, full of vigor and ideas and surprises.

She often came to me in the kitchen to tell about a run she had had in the fields or woods, where "the moss was like velvet," and the trees made arches of bright leaves. Once she told how she stopped at the end of a woodsy walk and saw sunshine over the meadows. "It seemed like going through a dark life or grave into heaven beyond. A very strange and solemn feeling came over me as I stood there, with no sound but the rustle of the pines, no one near me, and the sun so glorious, as for me alone. It seemed as if I *felt* God as I never did before, and I prayed in my heart that I might keep that happy sense of nearness all my life."

One day, after she had been quiet in her room for several hours, she ran out to help me take down the washing. A gentle breeze was blowing through the bright green tops of the trees, and the grounds around Hillside, tended so lovingly by my husband, made the place look like a corner of paradise. "We won't ever have to move again, will we?" Louisa demanded suddenly. "Because if we move I'll have to give up my room. And it's the best thing I ever had."

I had been going through my usual struggle with finances that week. "I *hope* we can stay at Hillside," I answered. I did not want her to count on it too heavily. "It seems to be a habit of the Alcotts to move, though, Louy."

She looked at me closely. She must have seen the worry-lines on my face. "I'll get the other clothes basket," she said. In a few minutes she was back, carrying the basket by one handle, her other hand behind her back. She let the basket thump to the ground. "Guess what I've got, Marmee," she said.

"One of your 'beautiful' bugs?"

She opened her hand. It was full of small hoarded coins, fifty cents in all, which she had earned sewing doll clothes. "It's not much. But it's a start. I'll put everything I earn toward staying here at Hillside."

My voice quavered a little as I thanked her. She was learning about family straits early in life.

But our financial troubles were only part of our life. We had books to read aloud and discuss, and our table talk, and social times with the Emersons and other friends, and walks, and reform movements in which we were interested. We had, of course, kept up our active interest in the abolitionist issue. I belonged to the Women's Anti-Slavery Society in Concord and took part in its activities with great conviction and enthusiasm.

The second summer we lived at Hillside the women held their annual picnic, commemorating the freeing of the West Indian slaves, at Henry Thoreau's little house at Walden Pond. For years Henry's mother had been one of the prime movers of the Society, and Henry himself was an ardent abolitionist and conductor on the Underground Railroad. Often he took runaways to his mother's in the dark at night, and from there conducted them along their way toward Canada.

In February of '47 we Alcotts had a runaway slave from Maryland with us for two weeks. He had made several stops on the Underground Railroad before reaching Hillside, and we suggested that he needed a good rest before proceeding on his journey. I warned the girls not to breathe a word to their friends about the stranger at our house.

Louisa sensed the drama of the situation immediately, and asked in an anxious whisper, "But what if they come looking for him? Where can we hide him?" I had been wondering about that myself. "I know!" Louisa continued, her dark eyes sparkling with excitement. "There's that secret closet in the back bedroom next to the chimney. No one would think of looking there."

As it turned out we had no need for a hiding place. Our dark friend, with cap pulled down, even helped Mr. Alcott saw and pile wood in perfect safety. I was sure that Louisa kept careful watch from some vantage point, ready to give warning if anyone approached.

The runaway was about thirty years old, strong and self-reliant and full of courage. His tales of the wrongs and sufferings he had endured in Maryland made a deep impression on the girls and reinforced their feeling of the dreadful injustice of slavery. After he had been with us about two weeks, he felt he should be on his way to Canada and freedom, and we did what we could to help him toward his goal.

The third year we lived at Hillside our financial problems seemed worse than ever. Louisa sensed my worry more than any of the other girls. One day when we were alone together she asked suddenly, "Do you know what my greatest wish in life is?"

"To be famous? To make a happy marriage? To travel in Europe?"

"Bigger than any of those," Louisa replied. "To make enough money to pay off *all our debts.*"

I laughed. "Aren't you a little young to be thinking of making so much money, Louy?"

I kept hoping that we would, in some way, be able to remain at Hillside. "Hope, and keep busy," I had found was the best motto for a family like ours. While we hoped for money to come in, we kept busy, forgetting our needs in our accomplishments.

I had long since discovered that no matter how poor one was there were always those who were poorer. The girls came home one day telling of a little girl they had talked to on the way to the village. The child had had nothing to eat all day. Next morning we decided to carry our breakfast to the starving family, and although it was only simple fare, to them it was a feast.

We were not the only ones beset with financial

troubles that year. In August the dream of George and Sophia Ripley came to an end when Brook Farm, in its seventh year of life, dissolved. They had lost all their money in the venture and were heavily in debt besides.

"What will become of them now?" I asked my husband.

"I understand they are going to New York. Mr. Ripley will keep on with his writing, and his wife hopes to find a teaching position. Somehow or other they say they will pay off their debts."

"My heart goes out to them," I murmured.

Along with debts, Louisa was a problem. She was in a particularly difficult stage, posing a trial especially for her father, who found it hard to understand his dark-eyed daughter. She would be moodily silent for hours, even days at a time, not even answering when spoken to. Then again she would burst forth so crossly and tempestuously we wished she were silent again. For a while her father thought she must be possessed by the devil, bound in chains that she seemed unable to break. I thought her actions not too difficult to explain. She was obviously much under the spell of the romantic reading she was doing, and she let her emotions get the upper hand.

A change for the better set in when she had her first taste of Goethe. In Mr. Emerson's library she came upon a volume of Goethe's letters to a young girl, Bettine, who had formed a romantic attachment for the great poet when he was nearly sixty years old. The romance fascinated Louisa. I learned years later that she immediately put herself in Bettine's place and Mr. Emerson in Goethe's place.

She became romantic, under the spell of the book, reading and writing poetry, keeping a "heart-journal" and wandering in the moonlight. She wrote long, endearing letters to Mr. Emerson, which she never sent. Later she told how she would sit in a tall cherry tree at midnight and sing romantic songs to the moon until the owls scared her to bed.

Of course, Mr. Alcott and I, and Mr. Emerson, were blissfully unconscious of the romance he was inspiring. But the venture into the romantic softened Louisa's moods and released some of the chains that my husband thought bound her.

The pressure of worry over family finances lifted for Mr. Alcott that summer, not because we came into a fortune, but because Mr. Emerson provided him with a congenial task. Mr. Emerson had been improving his grounds for years, adding plum, pear, and apple trees to his orchard, and having Mr. Thoreau and Mr. Hosmer bring pines and hemlocks and other trees to transplant around the house. He often sat and talked of an evening in Mr. Alcott's summerhouse, one of the many improvements my husband had made on our own place, and it occurred to our good friend and neighbor that a summerhouse on his own grounds would be an attractive addition.

Mr. Alcott was delighted to undertake the work. He felt pure joy in the task of creating an unusual little building in the Emerson garden. Mr. Emerson paid him fifty dollars, and as always the money was a godsend. But it seemed to me the work went on endlessly. For more than three months my husband put in long days, working on a bower in which he said his friend was to entertain the Muses, symbolized by nine upright posts. He went with Mr. Emerson and Henry Thoreau to Walden Woods to cut the hemlocks for these posts, and Henry helped for a day or two with the building. But the design was too original to suit him. It called for curved rafters, sweeping brackets under the cornice, and pointed arches over the openings and doorways.

My husband continued to work on this project almost till Thanksgiving Day. With amusement he listened to the comments of townspeople who kept coming to examine the building. Few saw it as an artistic achievement. "They say it's odd, Abba," he told me more than once. "They say it's the strangest thing they ever saw. A whirligig. But to me it has a beautiful simplicity. I prefer the curved line over the straight line in building. But Henry, now . . ." He chuckled. "Henry's geometrically-minded. He likes straight lines."

The summerhouse was still unfinished when Mr. Emerson sailed for Europe in October. In a way I dreaded to see him go. He was such an understanding friend, making books available to us all, taking us on walks and for drives in his carriage, asking us to his home on social occasions to meet his celebrated friends. Besides, he was ever willing to lend a hand in an unobtrusive way. We kept our financial troubles to ourselves, but he knew, of course, how little money we had coming in.

And how kind he was to the children, to Louisa particularly! She was an avid reader, and he gave her the run of his extensive library, letting her come and go like a member of the family. I could not imagine what life at Hillside would be like without the Emersons near by.

The day Mr. Emerson sailed, his wife, Henry Thoreau, my husband, and I went along to the wharf in Boston to see him off. The ship looked none too safe to me, nor to Henry either. We eyed it disdainfully when it could not even get out to sea by raising its own sails, but had to be ignominiously towed out. Mrs. Emerson stood bravely on the wharf waving good-bye. Behind my fluttering handkerchief I felt hot tears on my face. What if something happened to Mr. Emerson!

My load of misgiving and sadness continued until we learned that he had landed safely in England.

During his absence of over eight months, Henry Thoreau again lived with the Emerson family. He had left Walden Pond the month before, after more than two years in his "hut," and was looking for a publisher for his manuscript on the Concord and Merrimack River trip. The Emerson children loved him, and so did Mrs. Emerson in her grateful motherly way.

The children loved our girls, too, and spent much time at Hillside. Our barn, which we never used for sheltering cows or horses, turned out to be an invaluable haven for them all. They used it not only for a theater, but for "playing school," with Anna and Louisa for teachers. The summer Louisa was fifteen, she started what she called a "real school" in the barn when Anna was off in New Hampshire on a visit. Ellen and Edith Emerson, who were nine and six that summer, were especially eager pupils. They hung on Louisa's words when she read them stories she wrote about flowers or ants or spiders. Besides, she conscientiously taught them the three R's, even though she had never been good at arithmetic or spelling. The money she earned she turned over to me proudly, and I accepted it in the same spirit.

"Do you think you'll be a teacher, Louy?" I asked.

She shook her head. "Some of it I like—the stories, the nature walks. But I don't like all that sitting down over lessons. I don't honestly think I'm cut out to be a teacher, Mother." She stared out of the window for a few minutes, then turned to me pensively. "Do you think anyone would ever pay me for writing stories?"

"That would involve a great deal of sitting down, too, wouldn't it?"

"Oh, but when I'm writing stories, I don't *know*

I'm sitting," she replied quickly. "I don't even know when I'm hungry."

Fall in Concord was a beautiful time of year, and I somehow always found the peace of mind to enjoy the changing colors. But in late October of the year 1848 a disturbing wistfulness mingled with my peace as the yellows and reds deepened on the elms and maples. Soon winter would be closing in on us again, with its bitter cold and dwindling food supplies.

My heart clung to the happiness we had known for three years in our own home at Hillside, yet my head told me that the time had come when we must make a change. We had so often scraped the bottom of the barrel I expected it to fall apart any minute. What Mr. Alcott and I could earn in Concord simply wasn't enough to keep the family going. We had to face it. In Boston our chances might be better.

November was bitingly cold that year, the coldest the villagers could remember. I was beside myself with worry and uncertainty. One morning when the girls were at their lessons and Mr. Alcott at the woodpile, I did not make an effort to hold back my tears. Sitting at the kitchen table, I put my head on my arms and wept.

It was just at that moment that my old friend Maria Child arrived on a surprise visit. She had come to Boston on business, and decided to take the stage to Concord to see me. I looked up through my tears. She put her arms around me and urged me to tell her what was troubling me. I quickly regained my composure, except that the sight of my dear friend after many years, almost made me weep again from sheer joy.

I could not resist confiding in her. She was at once sympathetic and businesslike about our family straits. "Come to Boston," she said, "and let me help find work for you before I return to New York." Her confidence gave me hope.

Before the week was out, I had a position, and we Alcotts were beginning to pack our belongings.

One of the benevolent societies had hired me to visit the poor and decide where charity should be distributed. The work paid poorly and was very demanding, but I felt it was worthwhile. Without having a great deal to distribute, I had already been visiting the poor for many years. Now I had a chance to do it on a large scale. With gratitude I looked forward to returning to my home city, although it was a wrench to leave the home where we had been so happy, the first home of our own. We had lived at Hillside three and a half years, far longer than we had lived in any other house.

"Well, at least it isn't summer," Louisa remarked, as she went about gathering up her possessions. "It's easier to move when the leaves are down and everything is bleak and cold and gray. I just hope our prospects in Boston will be brighter than the November sky in Concord."

CHAPTER 17

WE HAD NO CHOICE but to move to one of the poor, rundown neighborhoods of Boston where rent was cheap. Even so we had to rely on Brother Sam to pay the rent until we could get on our feet. It was a dingy part of the city, with not a tree to be seen. How different from the Boston I had known as a girl and young woman!

Mr. Alcott also took a room next to Elizabeth Peabody's bookshop and ran a notice in the paper announcing a course of Conversations to be given there. He planned a series of seven Conversations on Man —his History, Resources, and Expectations. Single tickets for the course were three dollars; for a lady and gentleman, five dollars. With his usual optimism he pored over his books to find material. As for me, I could but hope that his investment of time and energy might net him at least two hundred dollars a year.

At once I began to pioneer in a new field as one of Boston's first professional social workers. I was forty-eight years old, but as eager about my new work as a young girl. I plunged into reading whatever books and articles I could find on the subject, to gain the needed background. I also asked Maria to send me a summary of the study she had made on the care of the poor in New York City.

My salary at first was the modest sum of thirty dollars a month. Anna and Louy managed to earn a little money by teaching, Mr. Alcott's Conversations brought in a few more dollars, and Llewellyn came to board with us while he prepared for Harvard. Each and every dollar helped to keep the family going.

I threw myself heart and soul into my work. All my life I had sympathized with the poor and unfortunate. Now I had a real chance to help improve their lot. I visited them in their homes, and solicited the wealthy for aid. In the first month I visited forty-nine poor families, solicited aid from twenty-two wealthy families, and had the door closed in my face in nine places. I collected money and, in the Relief Room set aside for the work, I amassed used clothing, bedding, and furniture; also some Bibles and religious tracts.

The needy who came to the Relief Room for help were not just "cases" to me. They were real people with real troubles and worries, and I could not help but think how I would feel in their place. It seemed to me that the rich were too severe with the poor: their hardness induced poor people to deceive because they felt that the rich had no love for them. How often I found it true that despair paralyzed the heart more frequently than hunger starved the body!

The plight of the Negro poor especially made me want to do all I could to help. They had so very little of the world's material goods, and so few of them had a chance at the schooling that would help them earn a living. Hopefully I started a sewing class for Negro women. But for some reason it did not go well.

Then with the help of Anna and Louisa I tried something else. We went three evenings a week to a neighbor's house to teach adult Negroes to read and write. They needed to know how to make out bills for the washing they did for people, if nothing else. They tried hard to learn, and all my sympathy would well up in me as I watched them bending over their tablets, trying to write their letters with pencils held awkwardly in cramped fingers. Even Louisa found it easy to be patient with the slow learners among them.

Several little Negro boys helped to enliven a Christmas party we Alcotts gave in our own parlor for forty children of the families I worked with. One of the ladies of the society provided the candy and candles for our brightly-lighted tree. Mr. Alcott entered into the fun by playing Santa Claus, and the happy Negro children sang like little angels, as Elizabeth expressed it. It was a day long to be remembered by us all.

My work did not end with the Relief Room, for people in distress found their way to our house, too. Some of them were forsaken children and young girls in grave trouble. We did our best to find homes for the children and to give new hope to the troubled ones. Occasionally friends would ask me how I dared let my girls mingle with these social outcasts. But the possibility of harm to my girls never worried me. I knew that I could trust them.

Anna turned more and more to teaching to earn money. Louisa took over the burden of housekeeping, insisting that Elizabeth, only fourteen, was still too young for the heavy work. Louisa also brought in whatever money she could earn by sewing, taking care of small children, and teaching now and then. The gloomy kitchen in the basement where she cooked, washed, ironed, and scrubbed made her feel like a caged bird, after all the vistas we had enjoyed at Hillside. She longed for the free times among the hills and woods of Concord. Tearfully she told me one day that the bustle and dirt of the city chased away all lovely images and restful feelings and kept her from thinking many thoughts. In time willing little Elizabeth took over the housekeeping, though Louisa rebelled at the thought. But, far from complaining, Lizzie found it developed her ingenuity to try to prepare attractive meals out of little more than flour, water, and apples.

From then on Louy was able to give her time to

sewing and to teaching. Oh, the endless sheets and pillowcases her quick fingers hemmed while her fancy ran riot creating dramatic scenes for some play. No sooner was her sewing done, than off she would run for pen and paper to write down what she had been imagining. She had a bad case of stage fever and dreamed of being a rich and famous actress, able to provide liberally for me and her father and sisters.

I missed my husband's companionship more than anything else during those busy Boston days. At Hillside I was always aware of his nearness—in the garden, in the orchard, in the library—even though we might not exchange ideas for hours at a time. In Boston I had to hurry off directly after breakfast. Sometimes I was unable to get home for the noon meal. Nearly always I came late for supper. And then three nights a week I was off again, teaching the Negro class. I missed our leisurely meals and table talk and sometimes found it hard to keep up-to-date on the activities of each member of the family.

I was surprised to hear how often my husband said, as he recounted the incidents of the day, "I sat and watched the fountain in the Common for several hours today. What a majestic leaping and falling of water, with changing lights and shadows!"

Momentarily I would bristle. Imagine having time to sit in the Common and watch the fountain!

"I am convinced," Mr. Alcott said once, "that the fountain is a symbol of something beyond sight. As I watch, fascinated by the perpetual rise and fall of the water, I try to visualize the mountain lake where the water began its journey. I try to follow it on its underground course mile by mile, until it reaches the Common and surges up into the light. Does it not seem to you that man has gone through just such a dark journey, looking for release? His motto might well be up . . . UP!"

I could not help exclaiming, "But the ones with whom I work seem to have so little chance to leap up into the light!"

"May not some of the beauty of the fountain be within *you*, Papa?" Elizabeth asked quietly.

Whether the perpetual leaping and falling of the water in the fountain wrought a change in Bronson Alcott, or some other influence even more elusive, I noticed that he suddenly stopped thinking of himself as a man in his fifties, getting old. He seemed to have found some fountain of youth. He straightened his shoulders. He walked with a light step. With youthful interest he began to look around for something he might do for a livelihood. Return to gardening or farming? Go back to the clock factory where he worked as a youth? Take to the road again as a pedlar? Go to England as a purchaser of foreign books?

I looked at him in amazement. Somehow he had found a way to stop the clock. Although his hair had silvered, never again did Bronson Alcott look old in my eyes.

The girls still carried on their play-acting when they had time. Poverty and worry vanished as soon as the end of a room became a stage and the world of make-believe began. Two favorite plays at this time were Louisa's "Bandit's Bride" and "The Captive of Castile," both highly melodramatic and filled with violent and unlikely incidents that helped all of us escape from the practical realities of life.

During the years we lived in Boston, Henry Thoreau would occasionally stop to see us on his way to read one of his essays at some nearby town. We were always delighted to share our simple meal with him. His very presence was refreshing. Henry seemed to have the key to unlock the wonder of every animal, flower and plant of the woodlands.

The day Henry's book, A *Week on the Concord and Merrimack Rivers* was published, he came to bring us the first copy. My husband was familiar with most of the book, and so was I, through having him tell about it during the writing. "Purely American," was his comment. "The book captures the very fragrance of the life of the woods and streams of New England."

We hoped the book would enjoy a ready sale. Henry had to agree to pay the publisher the actual cost of publication, and that meant going back to work at making pencils to earn the money. Sadly enough, sales proved a disappointment. Only about two hundred copies were sold out of the thousand printed. For several years poor Henry had to work to pay off his debt to the publisher.

Being single, Henry had only himself to worry about when he came up against financial difficulties. We Alcotts had a family of six to feed, clothe and shelter. That first year after we left Concord, in spite of all our efforts, we came nearer to destitution than we had ever come before. Even with Brother Sam paying the rent, we could barely scratch along.

I sometimes thought that, paradoxical as it might sound, poverty gave my husband wealth. It gave him time to do things other men had no time for. It gave him leisure to contemplate, to sit and watch the fountain, to go to Concord to see his friends, to read, to write those lengthy entries in his Journal, to converse for hours at a time. Through it all he remained fresh and serene.

Of course, I knew only too well that many people were worse off than we were, and my heart ached for them. I saw them every day in my work, like the immigrant mother and her children who came to our house one day to get help. They were all half-starved. I managed to find some food for them, and they sat in the garden to eat, like strange frightened birds. Poverty had ground the poor woman down in spirit as well as body.

I was grateful that poverty had not done that to us. Through it all we had kept our faith in the good and beautiful. We lived in a world of ideas, simple culture, and family rapport, and we never lost hope that better days lay ahead. We did not become bitter and disillusioned . . . not even when my visit with the immigrant family in the garden ended in disaster.

The unfortunate people infected us with smallpox! Our whole family came down with the terrible disease. Luckily the girls had light cases, but both my husband and I became very ill. Nobody came to see us, no neighbors, no doctor, no nurse. We had little in the house to eat, but somehow we managed to pull through. Later I learned that the neighbors blamed my husband, gossiping about his failure to provide for his family and his indifference to our welfare. I realized how he must look to outsiders, but I cringed to have him judged so harshly. His many gifts of heart and mind made him a beloved husband and father, yet they were not salable in the marketplace, nor were they understandable to the average man.

Before I had really recovered from our illness, Anna went to another town to help a friend who was having a baby. Louisa rather reluctantly took over the class of twenty children Anna was teaching at the time. It was often hard for Louy to be patient with the children, but they seemed happy with her and learned fast enough to encourage her to keep on. I could always tell when teaching became particularly irksome to her, for then one of her black moods would descend on her.

"You'd like to run away from teaching, wouldn't

you?" I asked one evening when she stood looking out the window at rain bouncing down the street.

"How did you know?" She turned and looked at me. Then, swept by emotion, ran to embrace me with a cry of contrition. "Oh, Marmee, I have so little time to write, and think, and be alone. But you have even less time than I. I sometimes feel ashamed. Instead of being cheerful and helpful, I let my moods get the best of me."

"You *try*, Louy. And you really have improved a great deal lately."

"But Father is right. You know what he said when he looked over our Journals. 'Anna's is about other people, Louisa's about herself.' It's true. But Anna doesn't have my problems, does she? She's so good she doesn't have to take care of herself, but can enjoy others. I'm always getting into trouble because of my quick tongue."

"I, too, Louy," I said softly.

"And it's harder for me than for Anna to be cheerful. So every day is a battle."

"I know about that, *too*."

"That's why I don't like to burden you with my troubles. You already have so many. But there isn't anyone else I can talk to."

I pressed her to me, my big impetuous tomboy growing into womanhood. "We need each other to talk to, Louy. So never hesitate again."

About this time Louisa was eagerly reading *The*

Scarlet Letter, Nathaniel Hawthorne's new book, which was being much discussed in the press. She preferred it to books that I considered more wholesome for a 17-year-old girl. But her fancy ran to lurid things if they were strong and true, and she felt that Hawthorne's stories were. Mr. Hawthorne wrote *The Scarlet Letter* in Salem and gave it a seventeenth century Salem setting. I could not help wondering if the book might not have been different had he gone back to live in Concord where, he always said, he experienced his greatest happiness.

We, too, had experienced happiness in Concord. Had we made a mistake to leave? For all our hard work we had found no more than a scattering of pennies at the end of the Boston rainbow. Pennies and smallpox and discouragement.

CHAPTER 18

THE LONG ILLNESS that kept us quarantined for many weeks had made it necessary for me to resign my post as a social worker. As soon as I recovered, I had to find something to do, and so I cast about for an opening that I could handle. Sewing brought in little money for the hours it consumed. The same was true of running a boardinghouse. I did not feel qualified to teach at my age, especially since most teaching positions were filled by younger women with more formal education than I had received.

Helping people in some way was the work I felt best fitted for. My almost two years as a social worker had taught me that the worthiest needy ones were those who wanted work and could not find it. So the thought occurred to me: Why not start an employment agency? I had already had some experience in finding positions for applicants who came for relief.

We all decided that an employment agency was a good idea, and for about a year my experiment worked fairly well. But at times my conscience troubled me. Occasionally some young girl whom I sent as a servant into a wealthy family would be treated most unfairly and even cruelly. This bothered and depressed me, since by accepting an opening to fill I tacitly recommended it to an applicant. And I was not willing to compromise with my conscience to earn money any more than my husband was.

The problem came to a head when a clergyman came to my office for family help. Louisa happened to be in the office at the time, and I could see her listening intently as the clergyman talked.

"I have need of a companion for my elderly sister," he said. "Someone of intelligence who can read to her and talk with her. Aside from that there will be a little light housework. And, of course, anyone who can fill the position will be well paid."

I glanced through my list of women and girls in need of work, knowing well enough that none could read fluently enough to qualify. They could do "light housework," yes. They could do heavy housework. But who would make an intelligent companion for the invalid sister of a clergyman? "I'm sorry. I seem to have no one to send," I was forced to reply.

Suddenly Louisa spoke up. "What about me?"

"You will come?" the clergyman asked with eagerness. "My sister will be delighted."

After he left I warned Louisa that she would be "going out to service," even though she would be called a companion. Her aristocratic relatives in Boston would be shocked. Louisa replied that she could not worry about that. Bravely she turned her back temporarily on her dream of becoming an actress and packed her trunk.

It did not take her long to discover that there was considerable *heavy* housework connected with the job, and little enough time for reading and being a companion. An old servant did the cooking, but the hardest work fell to Louisa. She had to carry water from the well, shovel snow, chop kindling, keep the fires going, and sift the ashes. The clergyman even ordered her to black his boots, but that she refused to do telling him bluntly, "It isn't a companion you want, but a galley slave."

She had agreed to stay four weeks, and she stuck to her bargain. Then when she was ready to leave, she felt so sorry for the poor invalid sister that she consented to stay until I could find another person for the position. I tried my best. The girls I sent would not stay when they discovered what they would be expected to do. Three more weeks dragged by while Louisa stuck to her post. Then she could stand it no longer. Resisting the pleas of the invalid, who slipped a small pocketbook into her hand, she departed.

Louisa left assuming she had been paid an honest return for seven weeks of the hardest work she had ever done. But when she opened the purse, she found only four dollars! We were all outraged, of course, when she reached home and told us her story.

"Four dollars!" her usually gentle father exclaimed. "You will return the money at once, Louisa. It is an insult!"

"If that man ever crosses my path again," I fumed, "I will shake him, in spite of his clerical cloth."

"I never had such a bitter moment in my life," poor Louy told us, "as when I stood there on the road in the biting wind, with the little purse open, and looked from my grimy chapped hands to those paltry four dollars."

Although we sorely needed the money, we straightway sent the four dollars back to the offending clergyman.

Some time later Louisa used her experience as the background for a story. She spared no details, and even added a few touches of her own, feeling that readers should be made aware of the deplorable lot of some working girls. She took the story to Mr. James T. Fields, a well-known publisher. He read it while Louy looked on, then handed it back to her with the terse comment: "Stick to your teaching, Miss Alcott. You can't write."

That pill was even more bitter than the flat pocketbook. But Louy, bless her heart, refused to be discouraged. All the way home she kept telling herself that Mr. Fields was wrong, that she could write, and would write. She resolved that someday she would write a story that he would be willing to pay for.

But first came more ups and downs . . . not only for Louisa but for me as well.

Louisa's experience as a "galley slave" made me realize that I could no longer take the chance of placing other girls in a similar plight. To keep my conscience clear, I decided I would have to give up the employment office and look elsewhere for a way to earn some money.

Louisa meanwhile resolved at all costs to find more time for her writing. Nevertheless it was a time when she needed someone besides her family to tell her that her work had merit, and it was our good fortune that a cousin of mine, Dr. Charles May Windship, was able to give her the encouragement she needed. The girls were all very fond of him. He often invited them to visit him and his family in Roxbury, about nine miles from Boston, where he carried on his medical practice. Louisa was more than willing to walk the whole distance to talk with him.

We were all in a flurry of excitement one day over a note I received from Dr. Windship, saying that he had offered Louisa's "The Rival Prima Donnas" to Mr. Barry of the Boston Theatre. Mr. Barry not only liked it very much, but said he would bring it out that season. He even predicted a fine run.

Some time later Louy had an interview with Mr. Barry. He took her all over the big theater and, even better, gave her a pass that would admit her to the plays there. Louisa's cup was overflowing. No longer would lack of money keep her from the theater. With a pass to enable her to see plays, she was sure she would be inspired to keep on writing more of her own. She walked the long miles out to Dr. Windship's home to rejoice with him over her good fortune.

To the sorrow of all of us, something interfered with Mr. Barry's plan of producing "The Rival Prima Donnas." It was put aside and finally forgotten. But the great hope Mr. Barry kindled in Louisa gave her inspiration when she needed it sorely.

Meanwhile Mr. Alcott's Conversations were making him many friends and attracting attention among the educated people of Boston. The financial return was showing gradual improvement, in spite of formidable competition from antislavery activity and protest meetings against the Fugitive Slave Law of 1850. We abolitionists fearlessly defied the law that levied heavy penalties against anyone aiding fugitive slaves. We protested vehemently, listened to speakers, and read the *Liberator*. Even Mr. Emerson spoke out at a public meeting, saying that the law was one that every one of us would break on the earliest occasion.

With his Conversations and participation in abolitionist activities, my husband kept busy. He finally seemed to be acclimating himself to city living, though I knew he deeply missed our home in the country. We still owned Hillside, for we found the place difficult to sell at a fair price. Mr. Alcott made periodic trips to Concord to try to find a reliable renter, to see about selling the hay crop or picking the fruit, to keep the place in repair, and to visit friends.

It was late in the winter of 1852 that a buyer unexpectedly appeared for Hillside, and it was Nathaniel Hawthorne who made us an offer. He had won fame, and, if not fortune, had achieved at least moderate financial success by the publication of *The Scarlet Letter* and *The House of the Seven Gables*. And he wanted to move back to Concord.

When it came to actually parting with Hillside, we hesitated. Mr. Alcott had put so much of himself into the place, and we had experienced such happiness there as a family. We held a council, as we always did when momentous decisions had to be made. Anna and Louy voted to sell; they saw few opportunities in Concord for making a living. "We had the best of it," Louisa said briefly. Hillside for her at nineteen did not have the same appeal it had had when she was a young tomboy. May, too, busy with her art and schoolwork, thought Boston offered more. Elizabeth loved the old house in Concord and the beauty of the grounds, but refused to voice her preference. She was ever ready to adapt herself to the wishes of the majority.

Though I knew it would be a wrench for my husband to give up his tremendous investment of love and work in Hillside, I could see no possible way of making ends meet in Concord. We had already tried, and failed. Meager as our living was in Boston, it was now slightly better than in Concord.

And so early in March we sold Hillside to the Hawthornes. They immediately renamed it Wayside and moved back to Concord. The money from the sale was put in trust for me toward the purchase of another house someday, and we Alcotts felt that one of the happiest chapters in our lives had closed.

The coming of spring that year brought relief from the cold and hardships of the New England winter, but it also brought deep sorrow to our family. My husband's favorite brother Junius, still in his early thirties, died suddenly. We found it hard to accept the fact that we would never again see young, kindly Uncle Junius who had meant so much to the girls and me during that long summer ten years before when Mr. Alcott was in England.

But spring that year had an unexpected bright spot in it, too. Something happened to lift Louisa's spirits, and it was our dear "long lost cousin" Llewellyn who brought it to pass.

Unknown to Louisa he took a story of hers to the editor of a paper called the *Olive Branch*. He waited anxiously in the outer office for the verdict. When the editor finished reading the story, he offered to pay five dollars for it, and Llewellyn gladly accepted for Louy.

Excited as Louisa was over having her first story

accepted and paid for, she and Llewellyn kept it a secret from the family until a copy of the paper arrived with her story in print. Then Louisa read it aloud to us, without divulging her secret. When we praised it, she told us the wonderful news. I had a hard time holding back tears of joy.

A poem of Louisa's had been published the fall before, but it appeared under her pen name of Flora Fairfield. The story occupied much more space and was signed by her real initials. We were all bursting with pride for our girl.

CHAPTER 19

OUR NEXT MOVE WAS TO a bigger house on Pinckney Street, where it was possible for me to take in boarders. I was prepared to do endless sewing as well.

At the back of the house on the first floor I fitted out a small room as Mr. Alcott's study. It was a cheery room with a fireplace and bookcases on each side of the chimney. We installed the much-loved busts and hung the old engravings. The thought of my husband being able to read and study in his little haven of peace gave me great pleasure. For his part, he often showed his gratitude by coming to the kitchen to talk to me, or read to me, or help with the work.

All of us did what we could to keep the family going. Anna went to Syracuse to teach in a private family. Louy started a school in our parlor with about a dozen children. Her father gave her needed advice and encouragement, and often read aloud to the class from *Pilgrim's Progress* or some other favorite book. When she closed her school for the summer, she decided to go to work in a wealthy country household as a "second girl."

I objected.

"Don't be so concerned, Mother," she replied. "I need a change. And I won't mind earning only two dollars a week, since my wages will be steady. Besides, it's all grist for my writing mill."

In the fall Louisa came home again, bringing her earnings of thirty-four dollars for the summer. After only two days of rest, she began her school again, this time with ten children.

With boarders to care for, Elizabeth and I kept busy at home from morning till night. May was getting along well at art school. And that fall Mr. Alcott ventured out to hold Conversations in cities of the West, a plan he had been toying with for some time. He went off looking "so poor, so hopeful, so serene," as Louisa described him, we all prayed that this time he would find some degree of success, more for his sake than for ours.

I found it hard to have Mr. Alcott and Anna away at the same time. But long letters from both of them helped to reconcile me. I kept telling myself that few families had enjoyed as many years of uninterrupted togetherness as we had had. And I steeled myself in the knowledge that more separations, rather than fewer, must inevitably lie ahead. Life moved on. Nothing could stop it. And much as I missed my husband and my girls when they were gone, I would never be willing to hold them back.

One cold night in February, Mr. Alcott came home unexpectedly from his western trip. The ringing of the doorbell wakened us. My heart leaped, for I knew at once who it must be. I ran down the stairs in my nightcap and an old jacket, full of girlish excitement, grown woman though I was. There he stood—tired, cold, and hungry, but as serene as ever. The girls rushed in, Louy, Elizabeth and May in their white nightgowns, and we surrounded him, hugged him, hovered over him.

Quickly and happily we fed him and warmed him. We hung on every word he spoke. He had done well, he told us, with the Conversations. People had listened eagerly and intelligently. He had, he was sure, laid a good foundation for other Conversations to follow. We longed to ask him if he had made any money, but we held our peace and let him talk.

Finally 13-year-old May could stand the suspense no longer. She interrupted with a blunt question, "But did the people pay you, Papa?"

I watched his face. A queer look came over it as he took out his pocketbook. Opening it, he held out one lone dollar to me. "It's all I have to bring home after expenses, Abba," he said with a brave smile that brought tears to my eyes. "My overcoat was stolen and I had to buy a shawl. Promises were broken. Traveling turned out to be quite costly. But," he added with his unquenchable optimism, "I have opened the way, and another year will be better."

I forgot all the hopes I had built on his success and thought only of comforting him. "You have done very well," I assured him. "And as long as you're safely home, we ask for nothing more. How we have missed you all these weeks and months!"

Louisa told me later that she never would forget the tender look her father and I gave each other. "It was half tragic and half comic," she said. "Father so travel-worn and sleepy, and you in that funny old jacket and nightcap! I could hardly keep from laughing."

The next month Anna came home from Syracuse and we were a united and happy family once more. She and Louisa kept on teaching all that summer, and Louy put in every free hour writing. She loved to write almost as much as she loved the thought of going on the stage. She might have been a great actress, for she had abundant talent, but I could not think of acting as a career for her. Private theatricals were one thing, and I encouraged her to take part in them, and in plays for charity. But I knew that professional acting was no life for a girl from a family like ours. In spite of Louy's disappointment, I was adamant in this.

On the stage of real life our own deprivations and

troubles receded into the background whenever we thought of the injustice suffered by our brothers with black skins. Mr. Alcott was active on the Boston Vigilance Committee that tried to save fugitive slaves from being returned to their masters under the Fugitive Slave Law. Several years before he had participated in the unsuccessful attempt to rescue Thomas Sims, a young Negro boy. And he had paced the streets at night to protect other fugitives from being arrested.

Then, in the spring of 1854, came the most notorious case of all, that of Anthony Burns. It rocked Boston from one end to the other. Llewellyn was boarding with us at the time, and he reported to me on meetings and happenings I had to miss because of my obligations at the boardinghouse.

Anthony Burns, a "slave preacher" only twenty years old, had managed to escape when sent to take a position, for which his Virginia master would have been paid. Three months later the fugitive was arrested in our city. Authorities tried to keep his arrest a secret, but somehow the news got out that Anthony Burns was being held in the Courthouse.

My husband rushed at once to Worcester to tell Mr. Higginson, a well-known writer and abolitionist, and they both hurried back to join in a rescue attempt.

The Vigilance Committee called a fiery protest meeting to prevent the return of Anthony Burns to slavery. Mr. Higginson thought that the fugitive must by all means be taken from the Courthouse. Finally a score of men tried to batter down the Courthouse door. When it gave way, they faced waiting constables armed with pistols and clubs.

Llewellyn told me later how Mr. Alcott risked his life and was willing to die for the cause of freedom. He was not afraid to ascend the steps of the Courthouse alone, exposed to danger from within and without, in an attempt to get support from the crowd to further the rescue. Shots rang out and a deputy marshal was killed. Then soldiers arrived and the rescue attempt failed.

When he came home for the evening meal, my husband was a crestfallen man. With an effort he opened the conversation at the boardinghouse table, then let it drift along without guidance. Later when we were alone, he told me something that made me gasp with apprehension.

"There on the Courthouse steps," he said, "an instinct seemed to stir within me, something that told me that to die was about the best use a freeman could make of his life in such a crisis. To die for freedom. I felt almost ashamed, Abba, to come back home unscathed. I restrained myself from rushing into the ranks that marched Anthony Burns down State Street. If only I had acted on this impulse, I might have aroused the indignant citizens into rescuing the fugitive." He sighed the sigh of failure.

"You did more than anyone," I assured him quickly. "And, thank God, you are safely home again."

For ten days Boston was in a turmoil. Finally the court returned Anthony Burns to his Virginia master and doomed him to slavery. When my husband returned home that sad day, he felt so crushed he could not speak a word until he said grace at our evening meal.

A few weeks after the excitement of the Anthony Burns case died down, Mr. Alcott sought me out in the kitchen before the supper hour. "Guess who I saw on the street this afternoon, Abba! Someone from Temple School. . ."

"One of your former pupils?"

My husband pulled a slim volume from his pocket and handed it to me. I wiped my hands on my apron. Turning to the title page, I read: "*Lyteria.* By Josiah Quincy. Josiah Quincy!" I looked through the book eagerly. "So Josiah has become a poet."

"A part-time poet, at least. He urged me to come to the office with him for this copy of his book, recently published. Actually, Abba, Josiah is a graduate of Harvard Law School, admitted to the bar this very year. But he seems to have as intense an interest in dramatic poetry as he has in the law."

"I often wondered what lay ahead for him," I murmured. "I shall ever be grateful for his youthful wisdom at the time we lost our son."

"Those were great days," Mr. Alcott sighed. "Those days at Temple School. . . ."

We were still living on Pinckney Street when Henry

Thoreau made us an unexpected visit one hot August day in that year 1854. He came to celebrate the publication of his second book, *Walden*, and we had the honor of receiving the first copy as a gift. The book had been long in the making, seven or eight years in all, for he had started this story of his life at Walden Pond while he was still living there.

At dinner that eventful day he told us in his humorous way that he had been careful to explain on the first page that it was not egotism but the curiosity of his townsmen, that had prompted him to write the book. People wanted to know what he had to eat, if he was afraid, or lonesome, and so on, and on.

I could see that Louisa was taking in every word. Now and again she was impatient about revising her own stories and plays, and she listened with surprise to Thoreau's account of his willingness to make changes. Polishing and revising almost up to the last minute, he wrote seven complete versions of *Walden* before it was published.

Of course, we all wished him well on his book, and hoped that sales would be good. And they were. Most of the reviews were highly favorable. For three days my husband immersed himself in reading and re-reading *Walden* with sheer delight in the witty wisdom that ran through it and in its Transcendentalism. Anyone who read it, he felt, would see that he could attain happiness and fulfillment by obeying the light within.

Before long Henry Thoreau dropped in to see us again not as naturalist, philosopher, poet, scholar or humorist this time, but as surveyor. His long-time friend Marston Watson had asked him to survey his country place at Plymouth. When Mr. Alcott offered to go along to carry the surveyor's chain, Henry quickly fell in with the idea.

They shared a room at the Watsons' while doing the surveying, and then Mr. Watson asked my husband to build a summerhouse. Again Bronson Alcott let his imagination run riot, as he had with Mr. Emerson's unique summerhouse. When he came home after being at Plymouth for some weeks, we heard all about what a joy the work had been. Silently, I thanked Mr. Watson and wished him joy in his summerhouse.

While my husband was at Plymouth, I had gratifying news to write him about Anthony Burns. The young slave had been taken to Virginia, although abolitionists in Boston had raised money to buy his freedom. A few months later he was sold to a friendly master, who in turn sold him to the Boston abolitionists. They at once set the poor man free and encouraged him to go West to school.

And so the year went. Better then most, and best at the end. That year at Christmas Louisa gave me a breathtaking surprise. I had an inkling that something unusual was in the air. Whispered conversations between Louy and her father ended abruptly when I came into the room. But still I had no forewarning of the unique gift I was to find in my Christmas stocking. Louisa's first book! With it, and equally gratifying to a devoted mother, was a letter in Louisa's handwriting. "Whatever beauty or poetry is to be found in my little book is owing to your interest in and encouragement of all my efforts from the first to the last; and if I ever do anything to be proud of, my greatest happiness will be that I can thank you for that, as I may do for all the good there is in me . . ."

The book, *Flower Fables*, was a collection of lovely little stories Louy had made up six years before, when she was sixteen, for Ellen Emerson. I was pleased that my husband had had something to do with getting the fables printed.

Louisa was paid only thirty-two dollars for the book, a meager sum for the work involved. But she was glad to have earned it by doing the kind of work she loved best. "In time I hope to leave fairies and fables behind," she told me on that unforgettable Christmas Day. "I hope to move on to men and realities." She bent close and whispered a postscript in my ear. "And to pay off all the debts."

With the New Year came the realization that, for all my work, the boardinghouse was not profitable. I would have to try something else, and that would probably involve moving again. With a sigh I sat down and counted up the houses we had lived in during the twenty-four years of our marriage. Could it be possible! We had actually lived in twenty-two different houses. I wondered if the time would ever come when we could settle down permanently, without having to worry about moving again.

Mr. Alcott talked about wanting to go to England again to hold Conversations there or to be purchasing agent for American bookstores. But I had not forgotten the sad consequences of his former journey, and so I had no encouragement to offer. Mr. Emerson outspokenly discouraged the undertaking, to my relief and gratitude.

We carried on as usual during the spring and tried to make plans for the summer. Louisa and Anna talked of going to the country as governesses. Mr. Alcott hoped to extend the scope of his Conversations in the East. It looked as if I would have to keep on with the boardinghouse, with Lizzie and May at home to help.

Then, unexpectedly, our plans took a new turn through the kindness of my niece Lizzie Wells. She asked Louisa to spend the summer with her in the resort country of New Hampshire, at Walpole, where she had a cottage. Louy left in June and soon was writing glowing letters about the beauty of the place, the freshness of the air, the attractiveness and vitality of the village. She delighted in being in the country again, running and skipping through the woods and up the lovely ravine. Spending her mornings writing, her afternoons driving with my niece, and her evenings in social and theatrical activities, Louisa's days were indeed full and happy. Her enthusiasm for the place led my brother-in-law to offer us a house he owned, rent-free, if we wanted to go there to live.

I was so tired from the hard work of keeping the boardinghouse that a move to the country almost seemed like a move to heaven itself. Mr. Alcott, too, thought well of the plan, for it would give him a chance to be close to the soil again. And so by July the entire Alcott family was enjoying life in New Hampshire in a little house not far from the ravine Louisa loved.

Mr. Alcott began at once to make a garden. The girls reveled in the freedom of the country. And for the first time in more years than I cared to count I was able to relax a little. My niece took me on drives in the hills and encouraged me to forget about our family straits for the time being.

For Louy it was ideal. Young people who spent their summers in Walpole had organized an Amateur Dramatic Company. They were an eager and enthusiastic group, and Louy had no difficulty in finding a ready cast for any comic play she wanted to put on. And there were many that summer. One evening an audience of a hundred people applauded one of Louisa's productions. Even the Boston papers commented favorably.

We had fine neighbors, interesting people came from Boston, and time passed quickly and gaily. I soon found myself enjoying a happy summer, involved in costumes and stage sets, picnics and theatricals.

Inevitably with fall, changes came that broke up our family circle. Anna was the first to leave, to teach in a Syracuse asylum for the insane, a position that Brother Sam had been instrumental in securing for her. Though she did not look forward to the work, the position paid well and she went with good grace. We all felt sad to see her go, sad to know that summer could not last forever.

The next month, on a rainy day in November, which Louisa called "the dullest month of the year," our Louy started off alone to seek her fortune in Boston. She was just a few weeks short of being twenty-three years old. She filled her trunk with manuscripts she had accumulated and clothes she had made from castoffs of relatives and friends. In her purse she carried twenty dollars she had earned from the sale of stories to the *Gazette*. "Oh, Marmee," she cried earnestly when she said good night to me on her last night in Walpole, "I want to prove that an Alcott *can* make a living."

"If any of us can, it is you, Louy," I replied. "I have not a doubt in my heart that you will succeed." I did not tell her how anxiously I would await every letter and what a hole there would be in my life without her.

CHAPTER 20

LOUISA PINNED HER HOPES on a new book she had written that summer in Walpole. She called it *Christmas Elves*, and May had illustrated it for her very attractively. But when Louisa arrived in Boston, she found it was too late to have the book published for Christmas. She wrote us about it blithely enough, saying she would put the manuscript away and try to get teaching and sewing to do while she thought of more salable stories.

Her cousins the Sewalls took her in, and she sewed for the family. I could visualize her bending over her work, her fingers flying as she hemmed sheets and pillowcases, her mind a thousand miles away, full of plots and episodes to write down in her spare time.

We knew from her letters what anxious weeks these

were for our girl alone in the city, determined to make
her way. She worried about Anna way off in Syracuse,
homesick for the family. She worried about the rest of
us marooned in Walpole, facing a cold and dull winter
after the summer butterflies had flown. She must have
worried, too, about Louisa May Alcott, although she
kept discouragement about her prospects from creep-
ing into her letters.

Before Christmas she had sold a story for five dollars
and earned twelve dollars by sewing. Eagerly she filled
a Christmas box for us at Walpole and sent it on "to
cheer the dear souls in the snow banks." During the
winter several other stories she wrote were published,
one bringing six dollars and two bringing ten dollars
each. How proud we were of Louy's progress, and how
we delighted in her letters!

Meanwhile, for the first time in years, I had leisure
for reading and letter writing. With May in school
and twenty-year-old Elizabeth at home to help with
the simple housework, I was spared the long hours of
heavy work that had burdened me in Boston. Like
Louisa, I could think and dream while I sewed. Mr.
Alcott, I knew, missed his city friends and activities,
and on the slightest pretext he would be off for a visit
to Concord or Boston. But I enjoyed New Hampshire that winter in spite of the snow and cold. I had
my usual worries about finances, of course, and at
times I felt concern about May. Shouldn't a young
lady of fifteen, with a decided talent for art, be given

more chance to develop it? Walpole offered nothing for her. Should I write my foster sister in Boston, the girls' ever-sympathetic "Auntie Bond," about May's talent and hope for the best? I decided to wait.

Spring finally came. On her way home from Syracuse in May, Anna stopped to visit Louisa and be mothered by her, for Anna was worn out from her teaching. She soon recovered, and the girls wrote of the happy days they had, visiting about. Yet a month that had started so well ended in tragedy instead of happiness. Once again I was to blame for subjecting my family to a serious illness.

How, I often wondered, could such things happen when one's motives were of the best? This time it was not smallpox but scarlet fever. I had been trying to help a poor family living over a cellar where pigs had been kept. Although the landlord was a deacon in the church, he refused to clean up the place until I threatened to sue him for maintaining a nuisance. The family was destitute, the children sick with fever. I brought food to them, and nursed them, and wept when two of the babies died.

Then May and Elizabeth came down with the fever. I was appalled to think that I had carried the dread disease into our home.

May recovered quickly, without ill effects. But our Lizzie, never too strong, had a severe case that lingered on and on. I did not write to Louy and Anna about it, knowing they would worry, perhaps rush home before they had planned. When they did come in early summer, they were shocked to see how thin and wan Elizabeth looked. They hovered over her, trying to anticipate her slightest wish.

In spite of everything, Louy managed to write a story a month that summer.

In early September Henry Thoreau finally accepted a long-standing invitation to visit us. He stayed with us only a day and a night, but in that short time became something of an authority on the local history of the village by taking books to bed with him. When he went back to Concord, he carried with him sixty-six new specimens for his herb collection.

Mr. Alcott had been working hard all summer, gardening, carpentering, and doing odd jobs. We all felt that a change would do him good and were happy to have him start off a few days after Henry Thoreau's visit to give Conversations in several cities and towns. He was bound for New York City where he hoped to get to know Walt Whitman. *Leaves of Grass* had been published the year before, and Mr. Alcott was one of the first to hail it as a most remarkable book.

Early in October we had a letter from our traveler saying that he had gone to Brooklyn to see Walt Whitman. "I spent several hours with him," he wrote, "and found him an extraordinary person, full of brute power, certainly of genius and audacity, and likely to make his mark on Young America. His egotism rather amuses me. And his genius makes me realize that Boston is not the only center of talent in our country. Walt, for that is what I called him from the first, has no admiration for Boston or Bostonians, with the exception of Mr. Emerson whose writings have meant much to him. To me, Walt's power at rest is like the great Mississippi River, and his poems are like that river, too."

Mr. Alcott was away on this trip for more than three months, which, he said, were among the busiest and happiest in his life. From the newspaper clippings he sent us, I could see that he was beginning to be known and respected as a speaker, and was no longer frowned upon for his untraditional ideas. In a small way his Conversations were becoming a success.

Louisa left for Boston in the fall before her father returned from New York. With reluctance she tore herself away from Elizabeth, who had recovered somewhat from her long illness but was still pale and weak. One afternoon when Louy was rounding up her possessions for packing, emotion almost overcame her. She turned to Lizzie and me with tears in her eyes. "Oh, let's ask the Lord to help us all and keep us for one another," she cried.

She was fortunate in finding a cheap room in Boston that suited her needs exactly. Mrs. Reed, a kindly woman who had been very good to me when I did social work, happened to have a vacancy in her big boardinghouse. Louy rented her "sky-parlor" in the garret for three dollars a week with board and fire. The house was full of boarders and Louisa found them an interesting study at mealtime. Her cozy attic gave her a chance to work without interruption, and she threw herself into writing and sewing with a will, never neglecting to keep in close touch with us by mail.

On Sunday mornings she went to hear her father's transcendentalist friend, the Reverend Theodore Parker, who always said something that seemed to touch her own problems. "He is like a great fire," she wrote, "where all can come and be warmed and comfortable." She looked forward, too, to Sunday evenings at his home, where she met many of the leading men of Boston and listened modestly to their talk. She managed to go to an occasional lecture, and to the theater often, on the pass given her by Mr. Barry.

Meanwhile I had broached the problem of May to Auntie Bond, and received a gracious invitation for May to stay with her in Boston while pursuing her art studies. That left me alone in Walpole with Elizabeth, who needed all the care and love I could give her. When cold weather came, we spent most of our time in the kitchen, the coziest room in the house. Outside snow and frost whitened the world. Occasionally the sound of sleighbells broke the stillness of the little village, half deserted in winter. The mail was the great event of our day, with always a hope of letters from Boston, Syracuse, or wherever my husband happened to be on his tour.

Louisa spent a happy birthday in Boston that year.

Auntie Bond gave a little party in the evening, and we heard all about it in Louisa's next letter. She wrote that May looked very pretty indeed—tall, blonde, and lively, and seemed to be a favorite. Louy, twenty-four years old that day, made a quick rejoinder when the boys teased her about being an authoress. With a touch of temper she told them that she would be famous yet! Afterward, I have no doubt, she regretted her quick retort.

Soon to Louisa's great delight she got a teaching post for three hours a day in a family where she had taught before. Now her board was safe, even if stories and sewing failed. "And I will have something to send home!" she exalted. The work was hard, but she enjoyed sitting in a fine spacious room part of each day. She also reveled in the luxury of her first silk dress, a gift from her Cousin Lizzie Wells. I smiled when Louy wrote that she felt as if all of her aristocratic ancestors beheld her when she went to two parties in it on New Year's Eve.

Early in January Mr. Alcott came home from his trip to New York. He had stopped in Boston to see Louisa, and she sent back with him a good bundle of warm clothing from Auntie Bond and others, and some treats she had saved for us. My husband was glowing with enthusiasm for his trip. I was amazed to see how young he looked. Except for his silvery hair, he looked younger at fifty-seven than our poor Elizabeth looked at twenty-one. He brought home a little money from his Conversations, after paying his expenses for more than three months.

"I was asked to come again," he told us happily. "And next time I will do better, I am sure."

He produced with pride a letter Louisa had written him for his birthday five weeks before. "How I wish I could be with you," she had written, "enjoying what I have always longed for—fine people, fine amusements, and fine books. But as I can't, I am glad you are; for I love to see your name first among the lecturers, to hear it kindly spoken of in papers and inquired about by good people here—to say nothing of the delight and pride I take in seeing you at last filling the place you are so fitted for, and which you have waited for so long and patiently."

Louy surprised us by coming home unexpectedly as a valentine on the 14th of February, bringing a breath of tangy Boston air with her. She brimmed to overflowing with her projects and ambitions. Such vitality she had! Elizabeth looked more feeble than ever beside her, though Lizzie's eyes danced with joy at having Louy home for a day and a night.

Then Louy was gone again, and Mr. Alcott left soon afterward on a second trip to New York. Along the way he stopped at other cities to hold Conversations, among them New Haven. There he talked to an eager group of students at Yale. One of the juniors, William T. Harris, became so absorbed in the Conversations on Plato and Plotinus that the whole course of his intellectual life was changed. In time he became one of Mr. Alcott's most able interpreters and defenders.

An undercurrent of worry nagged at my husband on this second trip, which kept him away all spring. Elizabeth's illness preyed on his mind. She of all the girls was closest to him. After his first trip, he had found her condition much worse than he expected. "She is wasting away, Abba. She is wasting away," he moaned, the first night he returned. Although I knew that she was not gaining strength, I had scarcely noticed the change from day to day being with her so constantly. But I knew he was right . . . our little Lizzie was wasting away before our eyes. It was enough to break my heart. I was the cause of the fever that had devoured the freshness of her life. I could hardly bear to think of it.

But the winter passed and the month of May brought more than the brightness of spring to Elizabeth and me in Walpole. First Abba May came home with an excellent crayon likeness she had made of me and a friend, showing that she indeed had the artist's touch. She had spent a happy, profitable winter in Boston. Then came Mr. Alcott, after concluding his trip with three Conversations in Boston. Anna again spent some time with Louisa in Boston before returning to Walpole, but by June we were all together again. Louy had achieved what she set out to do. She had supported herself, written eight stories, taught four months, earned a hundred dollars, and been able to send money home.

The only dark shadow over our happy days was our concern about Elizabeth. I grasped at the thought that a change to the seashore might do her good, and so in August I took her to the shore for a few weeks. Temporarily she seemed to improve . . . or was it only a mother's hope that made me think so? The rest of the family noticed no improvement when I brought her home again.

We held a family council, fearing that Elizabeth was slipping away from us. We all realized that it would never do for her to spend another winter at Walpole, where the weather was so severe. Nor would it do to go back to the dirt and confusion of Boston. Concord was the place. The fresh country air would be good for her. Though confined to the house, she would be able to see trees outlined against the sky, and she could look out on a thriving garden.

I was thankful that the money from the sale of Hillside was still in trust. We could buy a home, settle down, and give Elizabeth loving care and comfort.

And so we prepared to move again, back to Concord, home of happy memories.

CHAPTER 21

WE FOUND A PLACE ON the Lexington road right next to Hillside. The price was less than a thousand dollars for twelve acres, wooded and beautiful. It seemed to me that the house was thrown in, possibly for firewood. It was very old, nearly two hundred years, and so dilapidated that I wondered if my husband was right when he assured me he could redeem it. He saw great possibilities in the old structure, pointing out that the rafters and beams were still sturdy. I remembered how he had transformed Hillside, and I was more than willing to trust his judgment and ingenuity.

We rented quarters in the village while Mr. Alcott went to work with hammer and saw and vision on the home we were to call Orchard House. He talked of a central chimney and a new entrance hall and a new front gable, and numerous other alterations. Step by step, as his plans materialized, I saw how really artistic they were.

We were glad to be back in Concord, and hopeful that Lizzie would benefit from the change. Anna and Louy decided to stay home that winter to help care for our invalid and to relieve me from being so tied down. This gave me a chance occasionally to call on Mrs. Thoreau and Mrs. Emerson, and other friends I had missed during the years in Boston and at Walpole.

Mr. Emerson applauded our decision to move back to Concord. He had missed his talks with my husband. Besides, he was eager to have him develop new plans for improvement of the Emerson yard. Then too, he was writing a biographical sketch of Mr. Alcott for *The New American Cyclopaedia* and it would be convenient to have his subject close at hand. And for his children's sake, Mr. Emerson approved of having the Alcott girls back in town. Louisa and Anna at once began putting on plays and entertainments in the vestry of the Unitarian church, and they arranged for the Emerson children to take part in some of them.

The girls had two new leading men at this time. One was John Pratt, son of our friend Minot Pratt who had invested his savings in Brook Farm and served as head gardener there. John, a likable young man about Louisa's age, paid a great deal of attention to Anna. Then there was John's friend Alfred Whitman, a pupil at Frank Sanborn's school, unusually mature for his fifteen years. Louisa felt sorry for the motherless lad and seemed to like him more than other young men she knew. She even carried on a correspondence with him for some years after he left Concord.

At the end of October in that year of '57, Mr. Alcott brought home the first copy of a brand new magazine, the *Atlantic Monthly*. We found it good reading, particularly so because of its slant against slavery. When Louisa took her turn at it, she read it avidly from cover to cover, delighted to find that it relied mainly on New England writers. It contained two of Mr. Emerson's poems. "If I ever sell a story to the *Atlantic*," Louy exclaimed, "I will think I have arrived!"

With the coming of the first cold spell in November, Mr. Alcott decided to abandon his carpentry for the winter and to start westward on another series of Conversations. He planned to visit cities in western New York State and in Ohio. "Take good care of my girl," he told us when he said goodbye to Elizabeth. "I hope to see some improvement when I return."

Ah, but there was no improvement. As I wrote my brother Sam, Lizzie was so thin and emaciated, Louisa could carry her downstairs in her arms, and occasionally did so. But Lizzie always seemed glad to get back to the quiet of her room.

December came with snow and cold. Mr. Alcott wrote often, reporting that he was doing well with his lectures. Abba May took drawing lessons and worked hard over her art. Up until Christmas time, Anna and Louisa seemed to live two lives—the bright gay life of the theater, and the sad life at home watching over our invalid. They gave two dramatic benefits and a tea party for the antislavery cause with great success. But after the first of the year none of us seemed to want to leave the house. Elizabeth was indeed slipping, slipping away. . . .

Through it all she was calmly quiet, even cheerful, waiting for the great change that would relieve her of her misery. Anna took over the housekeeping so Louisa and I could devote ourselves to Elizabeth. Those were sad days and nights. Our letters must have alarmed Mr. Alcott, for he cut short his lecture tour and returned home before the end of January. Then he, too, took his turn sitting up with Lizzie. He told us one morning after an all-night vigil that he had asked her if she ever had thoughts of not recovering. Bravely she had answered: "Yes. I have thought it for a long while. It will be something new in our family, Papa. Of the four I can best be spared."

February passed, cold white days full of anxiety. March came with its blustery chill. On the night of the 12th, Elizabeth reached out her arms to her father and asked him to take her into his lap. He gathered her light little body to him and held her close. The girls and I closed in around them, and she smiled up at each of us, saying, "All of us here." We could not keep the swelling from our throats nor the tears from our eyes.

Two days later, at three o'clock of a Sunday morning, she left us. Louisa and I were with her. The strangest thing happened, which we both saw. Elizabeth had stopped breathing and we sat watching the shadow fall on her face. Suddenly we both saw a light mist rise from the body and float up and vanish. Somehow we knew it was the life leaving her.

We could not feel that death was terrible. In many ways it seemed friendly and wonderful. Elizabeth was now free from the pain that had racked her for so many months. She would never grow old, but would ever be her serenely joyous self in some other world we knew not of.

In the afternoon Henry Thoreau came, and Mr. and Mrs. Emerson. It was a comfort to talk with them about our girl. They had loved her, too, and we all had memories to share.

The next day Dr. Huntington came from Boston to read the old King's Chapel burial service. Mr. Emerson, Henry Thoreau, Frank Sanborn, and John Pratt carried Elizabeth's light little coffin to the carriage that bore her body to its new home at Sleepy Hollow. It was then, after it was all over, that Louisa, at the breaking point, went to her father for comfort. He gave her what only he could give—an inner peace. His sense of personal loss was as great as Louisa's, and because she knew this, she drank in his words and was comforted.

A few days after Elizabeth left us we celebrated Anna's twenty-seventh birthday in a quiet way, with a few little gifts and many loving wishes. Her dearest gift was the writing-desk Elizabeth had left to her, a desk Elizabeth had cherished and taken care of fondly.

For several months I had noticed that John Pratt was coming to the house more and more often. We were all very fond of him, but I could see readily enough that Anna was the magnet that drew him, and I could read a new tenderness in her eyes. She often visited John's parents who had a farm near Concord.

After one of her visits to the Pratt farm, Anna came home looking especially radiant. She sought out her father in his study. Soon he came to tell me that she had revealed her love for John and his for her. We had no doubt that John would make a good husband for her, but Mr. Alcott confessed that the thought of Anna leaving us, so soon after Elizabeth's death, was more than he could bear at the moment. Louisa, too, felt that she could not face losing Anna right then.

As for me, instead of losing a daughter I felt I would be gaining a son. Actually, John and Anna had no thought of rushing into marriage. They planned to wait at least a year. This pleased us all.

A month after Elizabeth's death, we were able to rent Hillside, now called Wayside, from the Hawthornes who were in Europe. This meant living right next door to Orchard House where Mr. Alcott and his helper were busy making the old house livable. Only a stretch of lawn, an avenue of trees and a gate separated the two places. Together my husband and I argued with the carpenter and mason to get the changes we wanted. Work went slowly, and not until July were we able to move into our new home.

I could scarcely believe it was the same house we had bought the fall before. It was beautiful now, inside and out. Besides, it was homelike, with window seats in the parlor and bedchambers, and ample fireplaces with big chimney tops. Two great elms overshadowed the house and gave dignity to the yard. I agreed with my husband that the site was hardly surpassed by any on the old road to Boston.

After Mr. Alcott removed an ancient barn on the place, we had a full view of the willows by Mill Brook and of the landscape beyond. Hills green with pines rose in the background, and orchards on the slopes came down to the road beside the lawn. And it was ours! I hoped fervently that we would never have to move again.

No sooner were we settled than friends came to call and to admire. Several came from Boston, including John Greenleaf Whittier whom we had first met that evening years before when we visited Mr. Garrison in jail. In the meantime Mr. Whittier's reputation had increased so much that he was being ranked among the greatest of American poets. Maria Child came for a visit, and she was so charmed by Orchard House that she wrote a detailed description of it for publication.

The girls had papered and decorated the rooms.

May used her artistic talent in painting birds and flowers on panels to put into nooks and corners. Over the open fireplaces, she painted mottoes in ancient English characters, with a special inscription in her father's study. One end of the long attic was partitioned off and sparsely furnished as a writing room for Louisa. There she would sit, free from interruptions, in the red and green cap she liked to wear. But for all the work she accomplished in her attic hideout, she never recovered her fondness for Concord. The village seemed cramped and quiet after her life in Boston.

She worked hard that summer, though with little success. She sold one story, "a moral tale," she called it, for twenty-five dollars, and used the money to patch up our summer clothes and bonnets. So eager was she to assume a major share of the responsibility of supporting the family, she became discouraged at how long it took.

Yet all was not work, either. On Monday evenings when we Alcotts held open house, some of the young men from Frank Sanborn's school would come to play whist with the ladies. We all enjoyed these gatherings, even Louisa, although she often tried to make it appear otherwise. She would usually start the evening by reading a book, off by herself in a corner. But I noticed that more often than not she would end up by joining in the activities. About ten o'clock I served ginger-cakes, and Mr. Alcott brought in a dish of his finest apples. I think in a way we were rather famous for our Monday evenings.

In October Louisa was off to Boston again, more discouraged than I had ever seen her. Work was hard to find. Stories were hard to sell. But I knew that her resilience would buoy her up, and a way to earn her living would be made clear. Fortunately she was able to get her old place as half-time governess, so her support was assured while she wrote, wrote, wrote.

After the first of the year, Louy was able to send money home, where it was sorely needed; and she even came herself for a week when I became so ill I had to take to my bed.

Meanwhile May had gone to Boston again to continue her art studies. She was different from the other girls. I saw in her some of the traits of my ancestors, particularly the Quincys, with their high-born manners. "A little aristocrat," I often said to myself. Mr. Alcott had started out on another western tour. And so Anna and I spent the winter alone at Orchard House, closing off some of the rooms to save ourselves the labor of heating them.

Anna, happy with preparations for her marriage, spent much of her time sewing. I helped, stitching dreams and memories into the sheets and pillowcases and towels. We both treasured those months together, talking as women do about the joy of being in love, planning a home, and having children to cherish. Anna, all eagerness for her new life ahead, did not realize what a bittersweet flavor some of those days had for me. My family was growing up and leaving home; already our years of being together as a family were in the past. I was nearing sixty, and to me that had always meant old age.

My husband's tour that year took him beyond the Mississippi for the first time. He had William Harris, the Yale student he had influenced several years before, to thank for an urgent invitation to visit St. Louis, where a lively group turned out for the Conversations. But the trip was a disappointment. The prairie country impressed Mr. Alcott as being the loneliest place on earth, and the Harris group proved to be too logical-minded to suit him. He came home in March, glad to be back in Concord again and thankful for its opportunities.

And what a splendid opportunity presented itself the very next month! He was chosen superintendent of the Concord Schools. His long-cherished dream of again being connected in some way with the teaching of children came true. Nothing in the world could have pleased him more. The salary was very small, only a hundred dollars a year, but it was work he loved, and he undertook it with enthusiasm.

May and Louisa had both moved back to Concord and were on hand to congratulate their father on his appointment. "Oh, Mother," Louisa said to me, "I'm so *glad*. Papa will do the work so lovingly and conscientiously, and being superintendent of schools will vindicate him in many people's eyes. He has probably seemed improvident and selfish to them . . . even indolent. And I will admit that sometimes he has seemed so to me. . . ."

"Never indolent, Louy. Your father has never been that. He has just used his energy in ways different from most men."

"Yes, that's it. But I often wished he were more like other men, especially when I was young. Now I am beginning to see the purpose of his life. And I love him for his infinite patience in doing what he thought right in spite of opposition and reproach."

No one could have been more conscientious in trying to build up the Concord schools. Superintendent Alcott covered the whole township on foot, visiting all the schools frequently, and walking many miles a day. He found great pleasure in talking to the children whenever he could; and he instituted the plan of putting on a school festival each year.

My husband's connection with the schools came at about the same time we met Captain John Brown, the great abolitionist. He had been in Concord once before, at the invitation of Frank Sanborn, while we were still in Walpole. This time we were glad to be able to attend the mass meeting at the Town Hall where he made a flaming, courageous speech against the evils of slavery. There was something majestic about the man—his tall figure, square shoulders, and face so alive with the burning ideal he was ready to die for. He had recently grown a flowing beard, which gave him the look of an apostle.

The Emersons, Henry Thoreau and his mother, Frank Sanborn and others felt as we did that John Brown was equal to anything he dared undertake in his crusade to help the wronged and oppressed. And we were glad to contribute something to the cause without actually knowing what his plans were. In a vague way we knew that he intended to set up camps in the Allegheny Mountains for fugitive slaves in the hope that they could be trained to defend themselves with the rifles and ammunition he was collecting for them.

Even though we half expected John Brown to do something of a violent nature, we did not expect such a dramatic act as the raid on Harpers Ferry that fall. My husband and Henry Thoreau happened to be at Emersons' on the October day in 1859 when word of the raid first reached Concord. They were stirred by the news and the realization that Captain Brown was willing to sacrifice everything for his ideals.

Henry Thoreau was so affected by John Brown's capture and arrest that he wrote a speech in Captain Brown's defense and delivered it in the Concord Town Hall. We on the abolitionist side all thought the address one of the most eloquent and effective Mr. Thoreau had ever made.

The question uppermost among John Brown's supporters was, how could he be rescued from prison and the death that faced him? Frank Sanborn and Henry

Thoreau thought that Mr. Alcott was the man to go to Virginia to see the Governor and plead for mercy, also to see if a rescue attempt would be feasible. But nothing came of the plan.

I had a note from Maria Child, saying that although she regretted the violence of the Harpers Ferry affair, she honored the brave Captain. She was raising funds to help his wife and three young daughters, and was carrying on an impassioned correspondence with the Governor of Virginia and the wife of one of its Senators. She wrote that she was in the fight till death, although she knew people were supposed to grow calmer with age.

For days and weeks all Concord was aroused at the thought of John Brown's pending execution. As soon as we learned the date, December 2nd, we planned a memorial service for that day. Mr. Alcott read the service for the death of a martyr; Henry Thoreau read selections from the poets; and Mr. Emerson read selections from John Brown's own words. We in the audience sang a dirge that Frank Sanborn had written, and a minister offered a prayer. Yet there was enough opposition to abolitionists in our little town that the selectmen would not allow the bell to be tolled for the service.

Louisa, too, had a part in the general memorial. She wrote some verses on the execution of "Saint John the Just," and sent them to the *Liberator*, where they were published.

But having her verses accepted by the *Liberator* was mild excitement compared to the other writing victory Louisa achieved that fall. She had long hesitated about sending any of her stories to the *Atlantic*. But finally one day when her father was going to Boston, she gathered her courage together and asked him to carry a story to James Russell Lowell, editor of the *Atlantic*.

I knew the story well, "Love and Self-Love," for Louy had read it to me fresh from her pen and discussed it with me. She would often probe me for reminiscences of the past. She made use of everything . . . happenings, characters, sights, sounds, incidents, feelings . . . and she used them in clever ways.

The elation of our whole family was beyond description when news came that Mr. Lowell liked the story. He wondered if it might not be a translation from the German, since it was so different from most tales. Best of all, he paid Louisa fifty dollars for it, and asked for more.

CHAPTER 22

THIRTY YEARS TO A DAY after Bronson Alcott and I were married, our Anna became the wife of John Pratt. It turned out to be a lovely bright May day, with green in the grass and blue in the sky.

"The house is full of sunshine, flowers, friends, and happiness," Louisa exclaimed, "but I am not comforted! We lose our Nan."

Anna was a lovely bride in her silk dress, with John's favorite flower, lilies of the valley, in her hair and on her bosom. Louy, May, and I wore dresses of thin gray stuff and had roses as our flower. "Sackcloth!" moaned Louisa. "And ashes of roses."

Anna wanted to be married by her Uncle Sam, and he gladly came all the way from Syracuse to bless the union. Guests were friends of long standing—the Pratt family, the Emerson family, Henry Thoreau, Frank Sanborn, and Elizabeth Peabody.

We all danced around the bride and groom under our great elms, and when we kissed our dear one good-bye, unbidden tears mingled with the kisses. Louisa, noting that Mr. Emerson kissed the bride, told me wryly that she thought that honor "would make even matrimony endurable."

Late in the afternoon, after the newlyweds had fled, a long procession of seventy children came down our lane as a surprise, to honor the superintendent of schools. Mr. Alcott at once hurried to fetch a large basket of apples from the cellar. The children, carrying wreaths and flowers, stood in a semi-circle around him under the great elms, and sang a song Louisa had written for them. Mr. Alcott was much touched by this compliment to him, and Louy beamed to think the youngsters liked her song well enough to sing it so lustily.

I was rather amused at my husband's way of ending the celebration. He skipped off at full speed, with all the youngsters following him in high glee. Up and down, and round and round he led them until they were all breathless and weary. Then the children fell into line and marched off singing happily.

That summer Louisa wrote as never before, encouraged by the publication of her John Brown poem in the January *Liberator* and "Love and Self-Love" in the March *Atlantic*. This time she plunged into writing a novel which she called *Moods,* and for four weeks she worked like one possessed. I worried about her. For endless hours she sat at her desk in the garret, writing, writing. She ate little of the food I brought her, slept little, and sometimes even forgot to go out for exercise. I was relieved when she finished the first draft of *Moods* and put it away to season.

In September Louisa sold her second story to the *Atlantic.* She had modeled the heroine after Anna and the hero after John Pratt, and had put herself into the story under the name of "Di." To our surprise and delight, the editor paid her seventy-five dollars for "A Modern Cinderella." Louisa immediately took care of some bills and set about writing another story.

When I went to Syracuse that fall to visit my brother, Louy turned housekeeper for a few weeks. She wrote me that she "dreamed diptoast, talked applesauce, thought pies, and wept drop-cakes," but I had an idea that she concocted heroes and heroines at the same time in that active mind of hers. One day when Anna came for a visit, Louy read *Moods* to her. "She laughed and cried over it," Louy wrote me afterward, "and thought it was *good.* I'm so encouraged. I'll put on the finishing touches when I no longer have to make a 'burnt-offering' of myself."

May went off to Boston that fall to take art lessons as a gift from one of our generous friends. In December, thanks to her Uncle Sam, she had a chance to go to Syracuse to teach drawing. Louisa called May one of the fortunate ones. She always seemed to get easily the things she wanted most. But Louy was glad to have it so.

We spent a quiet Christmas that year of 1860, with no presents but apples and flowers. Anna and May were gone, and our dear Elizabeth lay in Sleepy Hollow. We were in no mood to care for sugar-plums.

The Thoreaus were having a quiet Christmas, too. Henry was in bed, seriously ill. He had been working hard all fall on a study of the succession of forest trees. In November he began making records of tree rings. On a bitterly cold day in early December he spent the afternoon counting tree rings on stumps on a hill near Concord. He caught cold, but refused to do anything about it. The cold quickly developed into bronchitis. Henry had promised to lecture to the lyceum in Waterbury, Connecticut, in early December, and he insisted on fulfilling the engagement, despite the advice of his doctor and family. He came back from the lecture a very sick man.

That was an unfortunate winter. I became ill myself early in January. It grieved me to think that Louisa would have to turn nurse when she wanted to be writing at top speed on another book. She had a knack for nursing, though. Cheerfully she dropped her pen, hurried to my aid, and within a week or two she had me on my feet again.

Her interlude of nursing was followed by another of her frantic bouts at writing, revising *Moods* this time. For more than three weeks she wrote feverishly, with only a short run at dusk for exercise. Again she found it hard to eat or sleep. Finally she was so worn out she plunged into a regimen of long walks, cold baths, and loafing. Her father was impressed with the book and said Mr. Emerson must see it. Nothing could have sent her spirits soaring higher.

Henry's illness continued. " 'Tis a serious thing," my husband commented one cold day when he came home from visiting the sickroom at Thoreaus, "to one who has been less a housekeeper than any man in town, has lived out-of-doors for the best part of his life, has harvested more wind and storm, sun and sky, and has more weather in him, than any. . . ."

Most of the winter Henry had to stay indoors to escape the cold that brought on painful spells of coughing. A change to the dry air of Minnesota in the spring left him worse off than before. We were all worried about him, remembering how our Elizabeth had slowly wasted away before our eyes. Surely this could not happen to such an outdoor man as Henry Thoreau!

Concerned as we were over Henry and the ups and downs of our daily affairs, we still managed to keep in close touch with what was happening in the wider world outside Concord. The slavery issue was coming more and more to the front. There was little doubt during the election campaign of 1860 that the Southern states would break away from the Union if need be, rather than yield an inch on the slavery issue. Between the election of President Lincoln in November and his inauguration in March, seven states in the deep South seceded. We were shocked to have President Lincoln come more than halfway to conciliate them. He even promised to enforce the Fugitive Slave Law. But the slave states chose war rather than compromise, and within five weeks they fired upon Fort Sumter. With that the terrible War between the States began.

Like most northerners, we hated to see war come. Yet Concord responded loyally to the President's call for troops. A week after the Confederates fired on Fort Sumter in April of '61, a Concord Company of forty men left for the war. Townspeople raised more than $4000 for these volunteers. Now, more than ever, Louisa regretted that she had not been born a boy. She would have liked to be in that first little band of soldiers going off to fight for a cause she believed in.

In the weeks following Louisa found it hard to watch the young men drilling, while all she could do was knit and sew blue shirts for the soldiers. We women of Concord all worked hard and long. A few weeks after the war began, three hundred of us filled a quota of five hundred garments in two days. Excitement was intense.

Despite the war, Mr. Alcott put on his annual school festival and wrote his yearly school report in great detail. He had not been happier since the days, twenty-five years before, when Temple School was at its height. Louisa always enjoyed contributing a poem or song to the festival, and she admired her father's reports, which she felt "made education a part of religion and not a mere bread-making grind for the teacher and an irksome cram for the children."

And for a while that spring the war faded well into the background in our concern over Henry Thoreau. He had been failing steadily. Refusing to take drugs, he stood the pain of his illness serenely. "The power of spirit over matter," my husband commented. Whenever Mr. Alcott or Mr. Emerson went to see Henry, he wanted them to talk about wild life and plants, rain and snow, books and men, just as if nothing had happened. He tried to keep busy revising articles for the *Atlantic*.

His friends did what they could to cheer him. Mr. Alcott brought him apples or a flower or an interesting piece of wood. The Hawthornes, remembering that Henry had enjoyed their music box when they first moved to Concord, brought it to him. I sent spearmint from our garden as a tonic, wishing I had something better for him. He was much touched by the devotion of his friends, and lamented that he could never repay them.

On May 6, 1862, Henry Thoreau took his last painful breaths. He was not quite forty-four years old. Concord, I knew, would never be the same without him.

Later that day Mr. Alcott looked up at me from his writing table when I paused at his study door. He was choosing selections from Henry's prose and poetry to read at the funeral. "This is a sad duty, Abba," he said. "He was like a son to me."

The war dragged on. We could see no end in sight. But, of course, we abolitionists wanted no peace until slavery was blotted out once and for all. We pinned our hopes on General McClellan only to be disappointed. One evening Mr. Alcott came home from an evening walk, chuckling. "I dropped in on the Emersons for a moment," he told me. "Mr. Emerson seems quite disgusted with the way the war is going. Do you know what he said? That some strong-minded president of the Women's Rights Convention should offer to lead the Army of the Potomac. She would certainly be as good as McClellan!"

That fall Louisa came to me with the problem uppermost in her mind. "It's been nagging at me for months, Mother. Young men are being killed . . . and many others are suffering, without enough nurses to care for them. You have always told me that I have a talent for nursing. Yet here I am hale and hearty, whiling my time away. I don't think I can stand it much longer. What would you say if I told you I was writing to Washington to find out if they could use me as a nurse?"

"I would not object, Louy. I would be proud of you."

"Then I am writing today," she cried, and flew to compose the letter.

In December Louisa's summons came. She was to

start at once to fill a place in the Union Hotel Hospital in Georgetown, Virginia. She was ready. Weeks before she had mended her old clothes and gathered her belongings together.

When the time came for leave-taking, I tried not to falter. I knew, and she knew, that she might never come back. As I hugged her close to say goodbye, all my good intentions suddenly left me. I broke down and cried. Louisa, too, broke down. She asked if I wanted her to stay, and I quickly dried my tears and said, "No, no, Louy. You must go." Then I found myself actually smiling at her . . . until the door closed and she was out of sight.

"I send my only son," Mr. Alcott said.

I dreaded to think of what was facing her in a crowded army hospital. And the pictures I conjured up in my mind turned out to be mild compared to the reality. Louisa wrote us in detail after she reached her post. The Union Hospital had been a hotel before the army converted it into a hospital. "A more perfect pestilence-box than this house I never saw—cold, damp, dirty, full of vile odors from wounds, kitchens, washrooms, and stables," . . . that is how she described it. All around her chaos reigned, with no competent head to set matters straight. Yet in spite of homesickness, heartsickness, and weariness, Louy liked the work and found comfort in tending and cheering the poor soldiers. She had real affection for some of the boys and suffered to think that their lives should be over so early.

Night duty suited Louisa best, since it gave her a chance for a morning walk. She felt the need of some air and exercise if she was to stay well. But in a few weeks she realized that bad air, bad food, and bad water were getting the best of her. Soon she was trying to work in spite of a sharp pain in her side, dizziness, fever, and a cough. She was trying to be cheerful in spite of feeling miserable.

We could read between the lines of her letters that all was not well. I tried not to worry. But the thought of Louy coming down with some illness five hundred miles from home was not conducive to sleep and serenity.

Before the middle of January the matron of the hospital sent word that Mr. Alcott should come at once. Louisa was desperately ill.

Her father left for Washington immediately, and I sat at home alone, waiting, waiting, wondering how things were. Would Mr. Alcott get there in time? Would he be able to help? Could he bring Louisa home, sick as she was?

She had typhoid pneumonia, and other nurses at the hospital had died of it. Doctors feared for her life. At first she refused to go home, having served less than a month as a nurse. But five days after her father arrived she had to admit that her army nursing was over.

How the long hard trip to Concord was managed, I have never been able to understand. But my husband accomplished the miracle. At last Louisa was home again.

CHAPTER 23

FOR DAYS LOUISA lay in her bedroom, consumed by fever and delirium. We hovered over her day and night. How changed she was from the daughter who had left us—how thin and pale and pinched, with great dark eyes in a white face! We lost track of time and forgot our own weariness as we tried to nurse her back to health.

Finally the morning came when she tried to walk for the first time. Her father held her by one arm, and I by the other. Poor Louy wept when her legs buckled under her and we had to help her back to bed. But she had the spirit to try again, and next morning it went better.

After a month of the fever, she was able to come down to breakfast one morning. She could actually laugh at the strange, drawn face that stared back at her from the mirror. We in turn laughed with relief and joy that the long trial was over. After that we could see improvement every day.

Louisa was still recuperating in late March, that spring of '63, and Anna was expecting the arrival of her first baby. On the night of the 28th Mr. Alcott hurried home in a blinding snowstorm from a meeting in Boston with the news that Anna's baby had arrived—a brand new baby boy. We screamed with joy, Louisa and May and the new grandmother and grandfather. "A boy!" Mr. Alcott repeated happily, shaking off the snow and unwinding his muffler.

Next morning I was off for Chelsea, full of excitement. What did Anna know about caring for a baby?

They named the baby Frederick Alcott Pratt, which we all thought would do very nicely.

By April Louisa said she felt as if she had been born again. Everything seemed so beautiful and new to her after the long illness. "To go very near to death," she said, "teaches one to value life. I shall never forget this winter."

As soon as she felt her strength returning, she began to write again, putting down on paper some of her nursing experiences at the hospital. I had saved all her letters, of course, and she found she needed to make few changes in them. They gave such vivid pictures of hospital life and brought in the pathos in such a natural way, they gripped the reader immediately.

The editor of the *Commonwealth*, an antislavery paper, was glad to publish the hospital material in installments. They were a success from the first. The *Commonwealth* could not keep up with the demand for papers carrying the installments.

So great was popular interest in Louisa's sketches of hospital life that two different editors asked her permission to publish them in book form. *Hospital Sketches* brought Louisa a certain amount of financial success and a great deal of acclaim.

She kept on writing stories for the *Atlantic*, too—stories with war themes, popular at the time. And she wrote stories of a melodramatic sort, for minor publications. I knew they were not her best work, and it often bothered me. Was her eagerness to earn money and pay the family debts sending her off on the wrong path? I did not like to interfere, but I hoped that she herself would soon realize she was pursuing a questionable course. Unfortunately, she could dash off these "blood and thunder" stories with little effort, and they brought her twice as much as her other writing.

One story for Frank Leslie's magazine won her a hundred dollar prize, which she exulted over. But she kept the news from her father, for she knew he would question having the magazine in the house. The saving grace, so far as the Alcott reputation was concerned, was that Louisa refused to have her name on the stories. And I agreed to keep her secret in strict confidence.

Actually I found it almost impossible to read these stories, so Louisa did not bother me with them. But when she would come pressing money into my hand unexpectedly, and kissing me merrily, I had a good idea where the money came from.

Louisa was the main support of the family now. For the first time our life was beginning to seem secure. The money from her sensational tales paid the bills and gave Louisa time to work on her serious writing without having to worry about finding work sewing or teaching. I feared she worked overhard. Yet every night I was an eager audience for the serious writing she had done during the day, especially her revision of *Moods*. There was much of the metaphysical in it, the philosophy Louisa had absorbed down the years.

How full our life continued to be! We kept on sewing for the soldiers and going to antislavery meetings and occasional social gatherings, and we sandwiched in trips to Chelsea to see the Pratt family.

Louy, of course, kept on writing. She worked over a poem she had written in the hospital one night while she watched at the bedside of a dying soldier. It was a deeply-felt poem about the much admired friend of her childhood—Henry Thoreau. She named it "Thoreau's Flute." When she read me the final version, I was greatly affected by it. In fact, I thought it so good, I almost exclaimed, "It sounds like Mr. Emerson, Louy!" Instead I said, "Do read those last four lines again, Louisa. How beautiful they are!"

She read them slowly:

> *O lonely friend! he still will be*
> *A potent presence, though unseen,—*

Steadfast, sagacious, and serene:
Seek not for him,—he is with thee."

"The Hawthornes loved him, too," I reminded her. "Why don't you run next door and read it to them?"

Louisa shrank from the suggestion. She had a natural shyness, never wanting to push herself forward, always hating to be made over.

"You might slip a copy under the door," I suggested, "and be safely back before they find it." And that is what she did.

The next day Mrs. Hawthorne came to ask if Louisa would mind if they showed it to their friend Mr. Fields. Mr. Fields was then editor of the *Atlantic*—the very Mr. Fields who had told Louisa to keep on with her teaching because she could not write. Louisa agreed. Mr. Fields accepted the poem and paid ten dollars for it. We had special cause for rejoicing when my husband said that one of his friends thought Ralph Waldo Emerson had written the unsigned poem about Thoreau.

A short time later Mr. Fields paid Louisa fifty dollars for one of her stories, "My Contraband." The year ended on a happy note for her. She had earned more in 1863 by her writing than she had ever earned before. She had proved she could write.

Yet the constant undercurrent of our thoughts during those years was the awful war that dragged on and on. I knew that Louisa suffered at the battle reports far more than her father and I did, for she had seen the maimed, the wounded, and the dying at firsthand. For a while she talked of going back to nursing, preferably in a hospital for Negro soldiers, after she fully regained her strength. But as the months passed she realized she would probably never be strong enough again to be an army nurse.

So instead she involved herself in one writing project after another during 1864. After many revisings, rewritings, and shortenings—which for her was a victory in patience—*Moods* was finally published. She received the first copies on Christmas Eve, to her great delight. She made me a Christmas gift of one, and I felt proud and happy to read the inscription: "To Mother, my earliest patron, kindest critic, dearest reader, I gratefully and affectionately inscribe my first romance."

I was so excited to have the book actually in my hands, in print, that I almost finished reading it that night before I went to sleep. Louisa's father, too, read the book at once and thought highly of it, believing that she had written a better book than she knew. But Louy wasn't at all sure of its success, in spite of the years of "labor, love, disappointment, hope and promise" that had gone into it. She felt it had been worked over and shortened too much.

The first reviews of *Moods* were very favorable. But after a flurry of popularity, sales fell off, and though Louisa was disappointed, she was not surprised.

Finally, in April, 1865, after four years of war, came the joyous news of General Lee's surrender. People went wild. Louisa, wanting to be in the thick of the "jollification," took the stage to Boston. There crowds thronged the streets, shouting, dancing, parading, listening to speeches. When night came, the city was ablaze with fireworks. Louisa enjoyed the excitement to the full, as a release for her long-pent-up feelings. But in one thing she was disappointed: she saw only a few Negro men in the great procession. Then she was relieved to see one walking arm in arm with a white gentleman, and her spirits rose again.

I was glad to stay home and celebrate the end of the war quietly. Without fully realizing it, I had overtaxed my strength in my eagerness to help. How many miles of stitches had I sewn? How many hundred bandages had I made? How many furlongs of yarn had I knit into socks and mufflers?

Suddenly rejoicing turned to weeping, when news came of the assassination of President Lincoln. The whole village met at the Church for the National Funeral. After prayers, Mr. Emerson made an address. Frank Sanborn contributed a dirge. It was, as Mr. Alcott remarked on the way home, one of the most solemn occasions our country had ever lived through.

Shortly after the end of the war, Mr. Emerson came one day with most disappointing news. The work my husband loved as superintendent of schools was to be his no longer. The Board had failed to reelect him and the evidence pointed to a political deal as the reason.

I was indignant. No one knew better than I how much of himself my husband had put into the work and what he had sacrificed during the six years of his term. He had even given up holding Conversations at any distance from Concord in order not to be away during the school year. I fumed and sputtered while my husband accepted the news in the genial way he had of rising above unpleasant things.

When we were alone he comforted me with the thought that there are always compensations. Now he would have more time to spend with his family, and he could put in many hours improving the house and grounds. And next year he could probably take a long journey to the West again to hold Conversations in St. Louis and other cities. I marveled that he could foresee these compensations in the midst of his disappointment.

Elizabeth's birth date that year of '65 was one of mingled sadness and joy. Anna's second child, John Pratt, Jr., was born that day, just thirty years after his Aunt Elizabeth whom he would never know. Anna and John had hoped the baby would be a girl, but Louisa was jubilant. She felt sure she understood boys better than girls, for hadn't she always wanted to be a boy herself? Now she would have two boys to delight in.

Soon after our excitement over the new boy in the family, we had another excitement. Louisa had a chance to go to Europe as nurse and companion to Anna Weld, a wealthy invalid about three years younger than she. At first Louy wondered if she had the temperament to be at the beck and call of a spoiled invalid day and night. But she wanted to make the trip so much that she smothered her doubts and threw herself into getting her wardrobe ready for the great journey. "My long desired dream is coming true," she told me gaily, as she refurbished her old plum-colored silk dress. "And, Marmee, don't you think the sea voyage will do me good?"

I was glad to see that the prospect of so complete a change seemed to be giving her new vitality. She had been working hard at one story after another ever since her long illness, and her father felt as I did that a rest from the strain would improve her health and bring back her endurance. The sale of her stories, of course, had been a great satisfaction. Yet I knew that her strength was not equal to keeping up indefinitely with the demand for new stories. In Europe she could forget her work and be free to enjoy herself. That was my consolation at the prospect of being separated from her for many months.

Louisa's letters were almost as good as having talks with her. How freshly she wrote, and with what spark! We read her letters aloud, and to ourselves, and to our guests, and never tired of them. Her descriptions made us feel as if we were seeing all the places with her. And how faithful she was about writing.

When the travelers reached a Swiss town where Miss Weld planned to spend several weeks taking a cure, the tone of Louisa's letters began to change. We detected a happy new note. Louy spoke often of Ladislas, a young Polish lad whom she was soon calling Laddie. He was staying at the same *pension* and was obviously very attentive to her. Louisa painted him as a romantic figure, taller than she and very handsome, an exile from his country for having taken part in an insurrection against Russian rule.

I could see that Louisa's sympathy was aroused at once by Laddie's paleness and the cough that troubled him. Long months in a dungeon had given him lung trouble; and though he made light of it, all the ladies pampered him. Miss Weld was greatly attracted to him, too, and the three of them spent many happy hours together.

We gathered from Louisa's letters that Laddie had an unusual amount of grace and charm. He was delightfully entertaining whether he talked of his exciting experiences during the insurrection or played the piano, which he loved to do every evening.

Was this romance for our dark-haired daughter? I wondered. There had been a few suitors before, but Louisa had insisted they were a strange lot. Only one had she thought seriously about, though she confessed she did not really care for him. But marriage to him would have meant help for the family at a time we desperately needed help. I had convinced her, though, that it would be wrong to sacrifice herself.

Anyone could see that Louisa felt different about Laddie. Though considerably younger than she, he was old in experience and maturity. Louisa blossomed in those weeks of close association with the Polish lad. It wrung my heart to have Miss Weld decide to move on to Nice on schedule. I knew what it would mean to Louy to have to part with the charming lad, to have her wings clipped and be forced to live at the slow pace of a demanding and often unreasonable invalid.

Meanwhile at Orchard House life flowed on as quietly and uneventfully as the slow-moving Concord River. Mr. Alcott, without any outward sign of disappointment over losing his position, soon adjusted to a rigorous regimen of gardening, reading, writing, and making improvements on the house and grounds.

He lavished time and love on a new front fence. Carefully selecting knotted oaken posts, he set them at intervals, with cedar stretchers and palings between, working them into unusual designs so that the effect from both the house and road was original and picturesque.

"I can't tell you how much pleasure building the fence gives me," he said one evening when he sat down to the table after a long day's work. "Neighbor Gowan stood around watching me this afternoon, as perhaps you noticed, Abba. He pronounced the fence unlike that of any other man's in the world."

"Was that supposed to be a compliment?"

Mr. Alcott smiled. "Well, at least he admitted it was as *good* a fence as anybody's."

"Good, and beautiful, too," I said quickly. "The most original fence in Concord. I can see well enough where May gets her talent in art."

After the turn of the year, Mr. Alcott started off on another series of Conversations in the West. For the first time I alone made him ready. We used to have such good times, all of us, getting Father's clothes in order and his bag packed, and his neckcloth tied just right, and his head full of advice about how to take care of himself. Now, with Anna married, and Elizabeth gone forever, and Louisa in Europe, and May busy with her art class, I had it to do all by myself without the merriment. I would be lonesome when he was away. Yet I knew it meant a great deal to him to make the trips, and to be able to come home and press some money into my hand.

As for me, I suffered more or less from ill health that year, though I was careful not to breathe a word of it in my letters to Louisa. It just seemed as if all those years of weariness and worry had settled in my bones to pull me down. Many days I let the housework slide and sat by the window with my workbasket and my thoughts, and books that for years I had had no time to read.

Louisa's letters continued to bring us joy and delight. After she left Switzerland and her dear Ladislas, some of the weeks were indeed boring for her. She had to bypass exciting places and spend the time in a stuffy room waiting on Miss Weld and pampering her whims. I finally wrote, urging Louisa to leave as soon as she decently could. I told her I would send her money, without saying that the money would have to be borrowed from my ever-dependable brother Sam.

A chance finally came to leave Miss Weld in good hands. So off our Louy went happily and excitedly for a few free months in Paris and London. Laddie met her in Paris and took her everywhere, and often his two roommates, Polish exiles, too, added to the fun. Those were golden days, and Louisa treasured them over the years.

But parting inevitably had to come. Louisa spent some weeks in London, seeing all the places she had read about, meeting people, and taking notes for future stories. And then . . . home again! No one could know what it meant to me to have her back after a whole year of missing her.

She remembered each of us with just the right gifts. To her father she brought Raphael's "School of Athens," and Stirling's *Secret of Hegel*, both gifts dear to his heart. And to me she brought an album of olive wood filled with pressed flowers which she had gathered with her own hands at many places on her journey. And she inscribed it with these lines:

> *As children in the summer fields*
> *Gather each flower they see,*
> *And hurry back with eager feet*
> *To lay it on their mother's knee,*
> *So I, by ruin, lake, and lawn,*
> *Found flowers in many lands,*
> *And gladly hasten home to lay*
> *My little nosegay in your hands.*

CHAPTER 24

"I'M GLAD YOU DIDN'T TELL ME you had to borrow the money, Mother. I would have worried and felt guilty about staying so long. Now I'm ready and eager to write all kinds of stories to pay the money back, and more, too." With that Louisa retired to her garret, and she might as well have gone on another trip for all the company she was for some weeks. Orders for stories had piled up, and I was glad to see that some of her old energy had returned. If only, I thought, she could be moderate about her hours of work! But one might as well ask the breeze not to blow.

One August afternoon while Louisa was sequestered in her garret hideout, and May was occupied with a painting class in the village, I sat alone in my favorite chair by the window with a lap full of sewing.

Mr. Alcott had gone off on one of his speaking tours and did not expect to return until late the next month. The house was quiet, the humidity oppressive. I caught myself nodding over my work, though I tried not to give in to it.

The click of the gate roused me from one of my nods. I glanced out to see a tall, slightly stooped figure approaching. Mr. Emerson! How much older he looked at sixty-three than Mr. Alcott did at nearly sixty-seven! Why, I wondered, was he coming to call when he knew my husband was away? To borrow a book perhaps?

"You are alone, Mrs. Alcott?" was his question after our exchange of greetings. "Good! I have come to talk to you about your husband. I had an evening with him in New York recently."

"He is all right?" I asked anxiously.

"I have never seen him in better form. I attended a Conversation he held with New York ladies."

"Were they a good audience?"

"No! Most of the time they did not even understand what he was saying, yet they kept interrupting with the most trivial comments."

"He is used to that. He does not discourage the questions, you know."

"True. But they ought to sit quietly and listen with gratitude to a man like Bronson Alcott whose light is so clear. It struck me again that night that your husband is a man of singular superiority, Mrs. Alcott, and

I wanted to tell you so. As a man of pure intellect, I have never seen his equal. What he sees and says is like astronomy, real and vast, every part in eternal connection with the whole."

I dropped my sewing and sat gathering Mr. Emerson's words like pearls.

"That and more I have written in my Journal," Mr. Emerson went on. "And that is what I have walked over to tell you. But the moral benefits of a mind like your husband's cannot be told."

"Thank you, Mr. Emerson. I have known it ever since I first met him almost forty years ago. But I never had your facility for putting it into words."

After Mr. Emerson left, I sat quietly for a long time, my hands folded in my lap, my whole being flooded with contentment. What greater success could my husband have achieved than this friendship with Mr. Emerson that had endured and deepened through the years?

Louy's stories were bringing more money now. Before long the travel debt was paid and some of the household bills as well, and Louisa was well on the way to wearing herself out. Then I became ill. It seemed almost providential for me suddenly to need nursing care and for the house to need a housekeeper. Louisa put down her pen and left her garret.

In a few weeks I felt better. Louisa found help, and was able to get back to her writing. Then Mr. Alcott came back from his tour of the West with two hundred dollars to give me. A considerable amount, I thought. Besides, the trip had been a success for him in other ways. He came back with a much more favorable impression of the West than on his first trip seven years before. And he actually seemed to be rejuvenated by the experience.

With the coming of the new year of 1867, it was Louisa's turn to be ill, from overwork. But as soon as she felt better, she drove herself on again, bending over her writing pad for hours without end. It seemed to be an obsession with her to pay off the debts our family still owed. I preached moderation and patience, and for a few days at a time my words had some effect. But then Louy would be off again on her old schedule, working fourteen hours at a stretch.

Toward the end of the summer Louisa came to me one afternoon with two letters in her hand. "Which would you choose?" she asked, shaking the letters at me. "Here is a letter from Mr. Niles, editor at Roberts Brothers, suggesting that I write a book for girls. And here is a letter asking me to be editor of a children's magazine, *Merry's Museum*, for five hundred dollars a year."

"Oh, Louy!" I exclaimed. "How splendid. You must do the one that appeals to you most."

"But neither appeals to me," Louisa said bluntly. "A girls' story! I never liked girls or knew many except the ones in our own family. I've always liked boys better. And I *think* more like a boy, and feel more like one, and act like one. You've always said so yourself, Marmee."

"But the girls in our own family, Louy . . . you know a great deal about them."

"Would anyone be interested? I doubt it."

"What about the children's magazine then? What would it entail?"

"I'd have to read and select manuscripts for each issue, and write a story a month myself . . . probably more, and think of an editorial. To have time for all that I'd have to go back to Boston. Actually I don't know how good I'd be at it, either. I haven't thought about children's stories for years. But five hundred dollars. . . ."

"Well, if neither appeals to you . . ." I began.

"I'll try them both!" Louisa finished.

In October Louisa moved to Boston with some of the furniture she had bought, to set up housekeeping near the publishers. Our tomboy still, though almost thirty-five years old, she rode on the load, feeling as if she were going to "camp out in a new country." She had a great plan in her mind, which she confided to me before she left, to make a thousand dollars the coming year. "I want you to have comforts and to enjoy yourselves, you and Papa," she said. "You must see that our Plato never wants for new socks, and that his clothes do not get shiny."

Quickly I pointed out that earning a thousand dollars a year was far less important than keeping in good health.

Louisa became so involved in editing *Merry's Museum* and writing short stories, she seemed to forget about the girls' book she had told Mr. Niles she would try to write. Anna and May and I were unanimous in thinking she could turn out a good girls' story. Every now and then I would include in my letters notes of things that had happened in the Alcott family or in the May family that might be used in such a book. But Louisa kept silent on the subject.

Late that winter she packed her things and moved back to Concord, afraid that the work at Orchard House was too much for me. I in turn was afraid that she had been working too hard. I was aghast when she told me that in two months she had written eight long stories, ten short ones, read stacks of manuscripts, edited the magazine, and acted in plays for charity twelve times.

She admitted she could imagine an easier life.

One day in May when Mr. Alcott was going to Boston to talk with Mr. Niles about a book he himself was working on, Louisa asked him to take along a collection of fairy stories to show the editor. Her father came back with the stories. "Mr. Niles wants a girls' book, Louisa," he reported. "Something to meet the competition of a rival publisher who is putting out a series of boys' books. He says you promised you would try writing such a story."

Louisa sighed and made a long face.

"Once you get started, Louy," I said, "it will probably write itself."

"I'll start tomorrow," she answered somewhat testily. "But I won't enjoy it, I assure you." She turned to go, then paused in the doorway. "You remember, Father, when you used to go off on a tour, you would ask Mother in your letters, 'And how are my little women?' What do you think of that for a title? *Little Women*." She looked from him to me.

"Most appropriate," said Mr. Alcott.

"Perfect!" I exclaimed.

Louisa disappeared, and we could hear her climbing the stairs to the garret.

As usual she plunged into the project with an intensity that worried me. Yet I knew I would be wasting my breath to urge her to get a full night's sleep each night, to eat sensibly, to rest occasionally, or to find time for a good brisk walk each day. It was not her nature to rest when she had a project that excited her.

When the first chapter was finished, I will confess I waited rather nervously for Louy to read it. I was eager for this book to be natural and lifelike, with none of the blood-and-thunder of so many of her recent stories.

I needed to hear only the first four sentences to know that my nervousness had been unfounded. I sighed happily, delightedly, as Louisa's voice flew over the words:

"Christmas won't be Christmas without any presents," grumbled Jo, lying on the rug.

"It's so dreadful to be poor!" sighed Meg, looking down at her old dress.

"I don't think it's fair for some girls to have plenty of pretty things, and other girls nothing at all," added little Amy, with an injured sniff.

"We've got father and mother and each other," said Beth contentedly, from her corner.

In June Louisa sent the first twelve chapters of *Little Women* to Mr. Niles, a bachelor editor who had had little experience with girls. He was not enthusiastic. Neither was Louisa. But I thought the chapters very appealing indeed and urged Louisa to keep on in the same vein. "Girls will love the story," I assured her. "All I have to do is think how my own four girls would have loved it."

Realizing that lively, simple books were much needed for girls, Louisa plowed ahead.

On the 15th of July, not even two and a half months after she began *Little Women*, she sent the last of the manuscript to Boston, four hundred and two handwritten pages in all. She looked worn and weary and complained of an aching head. And little wonder. In addition to finishing the book, she had squeezed in the writing of three stories for editors who were waiting for them!

We who heard *Little Women* read aloud as the

book unfolded were excited over the true-to-life touches Louisa had worked in. There were the four Alcott girls, real as life, although I thought Louisa, as Jo, was a little hard on herself. There was Hillside, where the girls spent such happy days . . . and the birthday celebrations . . . and our beloved *Pilgrim's Progress* . . . and the plays in the barn . . . and the family post office . . . and the letters Mr. Alcott (March) wrote when he was away . . . and Jo's writing . . . and the breakfast we gave away . . . and May's (Amy's) talent in art, and Elizabeth's in music . . . "But, Louy!" I exclaimed, "you didn't do so well with me. You idealized your mother far too much."

Louisa only laughed and said, "You can't see yourself the way you are, Mrs. March. I can't make you half good enough."

I shook my head, unable to say more, for I knew my voice would tremble. I knew my eyes were shining with tears. Oh, what did those years of family straits matter now? Perhaps they had actually welded our family together with a special closeness we would not have known otherwise.

"And Laurie?" Anna asked. "Who's Laurie? Do I see something of Llewellyn in him? Or is he the Polish Ladislas you knew in Europe, Louy?"

"Partly," Louisa confessed. "Partly Laddie . . . the gay, whirligig part. And partly Alfred Whitman. You remember how often Alf came to Orchard House with John Pratt, after we moved back to Concord from

Walpole. Alf is the sober side of Laurie."

"Our little Elizabeth," Mr. Alcott said softly. "How well you knew her. You have made her live again."

"What about Laurie's grandfather, Mr. Lawrence?" May asked. "Where did you get him?"

Louisa hesitated, and I answered for her. "You were too young when your Grandfather May died to remember what he was like. But I can see my father popping out in the character of Mr. Lawrence. Though I think you made him a bit too stern, Louisa."

"Perhaps. But I had Grandfather May in mind much of the time."

None of us could guess who Aunt March might be. Louisa set our minds at ease by saying she was nobody in real life, just a character she had made up. Of course, we all recognized John Brooke as Anna's John Pratt, and how gaily we all lived through the wedding again, even to the lilies of the valley for the bride.

"I made up Hannah," Louisa said with a smile, "to satisfy a long-suppressed desire, I suppose. I never did like housework, you remember. And I always thought Mother had to do too much of it. Hannah was one of those luxuries we Alcotts could dream about but never expect to have . . . except in a story."

Mr. Niles accepted *Little Women* with a mild amount of enthusiasm after some of his nieces told him the story was splendid. By late August Louisa received proofs of the book. Upon rereading it, she found it was better than she remembered. "It's simple and true," she commented. "We really lived most of it; and if it succeeds that will be the reason."

Two Alcott books had a place on the Roberts Brothers list that fall: *Tablets* by A. Bronson Alcott, and *Little Women* by Louisa May Alcott. My husband's book came out first, in September. He presented me a copy with a gracious bow, and my joy was unbounded. It did seem that at last, as he neared seventy, he was coming into his own. I opened the book at random. My eye fell upon something about age, which I read aloud:

"The surest sign of age is loneliness. While one finds company in himself and his pursuits, he cannot be old, whatever his years may number."

I smiled up at my ever-serene husband whose pursuits were never finished. "You will never be old," I said. "But somewhere along the way I became tired and lost some of my pursuits, I am afraid." I looked back at the book thumbing the pages, until I was stopped by other words that seemed to jump from the page: "Faith and persistence are life's architects, while doubt and despair bury all under the ruins of any endeavor . . . We mount to heaven mostly on the ruins of our cherished schemes, finding our failures were successes."

"Yes," I mused. "Our failures did not turn out to be failures, did they? And our greatest success all along was our family, our being together. Oh, my dear husband, I hope the book will bring you praise. You have waited so long for it."

On the 8th of October that year I was sixty-eight years old, far too old for a fuss to be made over me. Anna and her two boys were visiting at Orchard House and that was celebration enough for me. After breakfast Mr. Alcott escorted me to my big chair near the study table. There on the table lay a pile of gifts. Freddy and Johnny Pratt came marching in, blowing trumpets, and behind them pranced Anna, Louisa, and May. I had difficulty separating tears from laughter so I just let them blend together.

The boys handed me my gifts one by one, each with a verse the girls had written. Last came a package that felt like a book. I unwrapped it, and in my hands lay the first bound copy of *Little Women*.

Late in October Louisa went back to Boston, taking a room this time in a quiet part of town. In a day or two she wrote me that she had seen Mr. Niles and heard good news about the book. The first edition was already sold out, another was on the way, and an order had come for a London edition. "And besides, Mother, Mr. Niles wants a second volume for spring. I shall begin it tomorrow. If I can write a chapter a day, I can finish before the end of the year."

"Dear Louisa," I murmured into my workbasket, "will you never learn not to drive yourself?"

Reviews and letters about *Little Women* began coming in. Leading newspapers and magazines without exception praised the book. By December Louisa received a payment of three hundred dollars. Instead of being paid outright for the book, she had accepted Mr. Niles' offer of a royalty on each copy sold.

In December Mr. Alcott went west again on another of his lecture tours. May wished to go to Boston for more art study, and Anna asked me to spend the winter with her. So Louisa left her writing long enough to return to Concord to close up the house. "We scatter like chickens," I thought. "Perhaps it will be that way from now on. Only in the summer will the Alcotts come home to roost."

But I was wrong. In March I felt restless at Anna's. I wanted my own home again, my own things. Mr. Alcott, back from his tour wanted his books and study table. Louisa and May saw that Orchard House was best for us, and so they came home, and we were our own family again, smaller, but no less close because of it.

Louisa, I could see, was quite worn out from her writing. Yet in her face I detected an easing of the tension that had long possessed her. Was it because she saw her way clear to earning the cherished thousand dollars that year, I wondered?

I said nothing, but one afternoon she came in almost serenely and sat beside me at the window. In her hand she held a few letters to be mailed. "When Father goes for the mail, will you have him post these?" she asked. "They are very important." She looked at the addresses, one after the other. "The last of the debts, Marmee! They are all paid now, thank the Lord!—all that money can repay. We Alcotts do not owe a cent in the world. My dreams are beginning to come true. If my head holds out, you and Plato shall have all the comforts money can buy."

I reached for her free hand. "Thank you, Louy. Comforts do come in handy when one reaches my age, but comforts aren't everything. I remember what your father has always said . . . that human life is a very simple matter. 'Breath, bread, health, a hearthstone . . . a wife and children, a friend or two . . . and a task life-long given from within.' And these are the gifts we Alcotts have had all along, Louy."

POSTSCRIPT

AFTER MOVING MORE THAN two dozen times in the early years of her marriage, "Marmee" had the gratifying experience of living in her own home at Orchard House for almost twenty years. The last nine years of her life, after the publication of *Little Women*, she had no financial worries and was surrounded by every comfort. Although she suffered from ill health and increasing feebleness during most of her later years, her spirit remained as indomitable as ever. She never ceased trying to further the interests of each member of the family.

When she was seventy she encouraged Louisa and May to travel in Europe for a year, and later urged May to take advantage of Louisa's offer to send her back to Europe for further study in art. Mrs. Alcott's last years were made rich by her interest in her two grandsons, in Louisa's ever-growing fame as a writer, in May's success as an artist, and most of all in Bronson Alcott's renown as a lecturer.

When Louisa and May were in Europe in 1870, they were shocked and grieved by news of the sudden death of Anna's husband, John Pratt. Louisa, vacationing in Rome, immediately set about writing *Little Men* for the support of her sister and her two nephews. Later Anna and her boys moved to Concord and lived in the old Thoreau House.

The name of Louisa M. Alcott became famous wherever the English language was spoken as a succession of books followed *Little Women: An Old Fashioned Girl, Little Men, Eight Cousins, Rose in Bloom, Under the Lilacs, Jo's Boys.* Royalties poured in, and Louisa was able to supply her family with comforts and luxuries in addition to a security they had never known. She had a furnace installed in Orchard House, the rooms redecorated, the old May heirlooms refinished, and her father's books rebound in handsome new covers. She was in a position to take life easy, but she felt impelled to keep on writing in spite of chronic ill health. Driving herself on and on, she died in her fifty-sixth year, just two days after the death of her father.

May achieved a certain amount of success as an artist, and was honored by having one of her pictures hung in the Salon in Paris. As she neared forty, she fell in love with a Swiss businessman considerably younger than she. They were married, and settled down happily in Paris. Soon after the birth of her daughter, Louisa May Nieriker, May died, leaving her daughter to the care of her famous sister.

Bronson Alcott's later years showed his perennial resilience of spirit. He achieved considerable fame as a lecturer, and as the "father of *Little Women.*" His books *Tablets, Concord Days,* and *Table Talk* achieved a mild success. In his eightieth year he realized one of his fondest dreams in establishing the Concord Summer School of Philosophy and Literature, which flourished until his death nine years later.

A month before his eighty-third birthday, just six months after the death of his cherished friend Ralph Waldo Emerson, Mr. Alcott suffered a stroke. Although he never fully recovered from the semi-paralysis, his mind remained clear and alert to the end.

Orchard House, one of the oldest houses in Concord, Massachusetts, is now a permanent memorial to Louisa May Alcott. In 1911 the Concord Women's Club decided to buy it and restore it, and sent out an appeal for contributions. Money came in from young and old all over the country. Relatives and friends of the Alcotts contributed mementoes and furniture, including the piano the girls used. The house is now furnished to look as near like the old Alcott home as possible, a fitting tribute to one of America's most loved writers.

BIBLIOGRAPHY

ALCOTT, A. BRONSON: *Tablets*. Boston: Roberts Brothers, 1868.

ALCOTT, A. BRONSON: *Concord Days*. Boston: Roberts Brothers, 1872.

ALCOTT, LOUISA MAY: *Hospital Sketches*. Introduction by Bessie Z. Jones. Cambridge, Mass.: Harvard University Press, 1960.

ANTHONY, KATHERINE: *Louisa May Alcott*. New York: Knopf, 1938.

BROOKS, VAN WYCK: *The Flowering of New England*. New York: Dutton, 1952 (Paperback)

CHENEY, EDNAH D. (Ed.): *Louisa May Alcott, Her Life, Letters, and Journals*. Boston: Little, Brown, 1928.

EMERSON, RALPH WALDO: *Journals*. With annotations edited by Edward Waldo Emerson and Waldo

Emerson Forbes. Boston: Houghton, 1909-1914.

FROTHINGHAM, OCTAVIUS BROOKS: *Transcendentalism in New England.* New York: Harper, 1959 (Torchbook).

HARDING, WALTER: *The Days of Henry Thoreau.* New York: Knopf, 1965.

HOELTJE, HUBERT H.: *Sheltering Tree, A Story of the Friendship of Ralph Waldo Emerson and Amos Bronson Alcott.* Durham, N.C.: Duke University Press, 1943.

KORNGOLD, RALPH: *Two Friends of Man, The Story of William Lloyd Garrison and Wendell Phillips.* Boston: Little, Brown, 1950.

MCCUSKEY, DOROTHY: *Bronson Alcott, Teacher.* New York: Macmillan, 1940.

MEIGS, CORNELIA: *Invincible Louisa, The Story of the Author of "Little Women."* New York: Scholastic Book Services, 1956 (Paperback).

MORROW, HONORE WILLSIE: *The Father of Little Women.* Boston: Little, Brown, 1927.

RUSK, RALPH L.: *The Life of Ralph Waldo Emerson.* New York: Scribners, 1949.

SALYER, SANFORD: *Marmee, The Mother of Little Women.* Norman, Okla.: University of Oklahoma Press, 1949.

SAMS, HENRY W. (Ed.): *Autobiography of Brook Farm.* Englewood Cliffs, N.J.: Prentice-Hall, 1958.

SANBORN, F. B. AND HARRIS, WILLIAM T.: *A. Bronson Alcott—His Life and Philosophy.* Two volumes. Boston: Roberts Brothers, 1893.

SANBORN, F. B.: *Recollections of Seventy Years.* Boston: The Gorham Press, 1909.

SEARS, CLARA ENDICOTT (Compiler): *Bronson Alcott's Fruitlands,* with *Transcendental Wild Oats* by Louisa M. Alcott. Boston: Houghton, 1915.

SHEPARD, ODELL: *Pedlar's Progress, The Life of Bronson Alcott.* Boston: Little, Brown, 1937.

SHEPARD, ODELL (Ed.): *The Heart of Thoreau's Journals.* Boston: Houghton, 1927.

SHEPARD, ODELL (Ed.): *The Journals of Bronson Alcott.* Boston: Little Brown, 1938.

STERN, MADELEINE B.: *Louisa May Alcott.* Norman, Okla.: University of Oklahoma Press, 1950.

WILLIS, FREDERICK L. H. ("Llewellyn"): *Alcott Memoirs.* Boston: Badger, 1915.

WORTHINGTON, MARJORIE: *Miss Alcott of Concord.* Garden City, N.Y.: Doubleday, 1958.